Agriculture:
The Triumph and the Shame

Richard Body

Temple Smith/London

First published in Great Britain 1982 by
Maurice Temple Smith Limited
Gloucester Mansions, Cambridge Circus
London WC2H 8HD

ISBN 0 85117 228 8

Typeset by Robcroft Limited
London WC1
Printed and bound in Great Britain by
Billing and Sons Limited, Worcester

Contents

Introduction vii

1   Two Sorry Facts 1

The True Cost of Supporting Agriculture

2   The Diversion of Capital 19
3   The Diversion of Land and Labour 38
4   The Diversion of Natural Resources 44

Is There a Case for Support?

5   Do We Need 'Security of Supply'? 51
6   A Starving World 62
7   The Strategic Argument 69
8   The Balance of Payments Myth 72
9   Conserving the Countryside 78

The Future

10   The Free Trade Alternative 87
11   When British Farming Flourished 99

12   The CAP: Why It Cannot Fit British Farmers 110

13   The Truth about Protection 122

14   Summary 124

Appendix 1: The Classification of Land 131

Appendix 2: Calculating the Cost of the CAP to the British People 133

Introduction

Many millions of people around the world simply never get enough to eat: hunger, malnutrition and starvation are the symbols of the Third World. Those of us in the developed world suffer from lesser problems: our bellies are seldom empty, but inflationary food bills constantly strain the average family budget. For poorer people this is a very real problem.

The conventional wisdom is that there is something inevitable about this. We are told that the inexorable rise in the world's population is putting an intolerable strain on food supplies, and so we must pay more for our groceries. Governments express concern for the starving millions, talk of the need for more overseas aid, and urge the Third World to do more to solve its own problems.

What we are not told often enough is the simple truth: that there is no technical barrier in the way of eliminating starvation from the world, even with a rising population; that our own food costs are pushed to unacceptable heights by the short-sighted policies of our own governments; and that these same policies, acting on the world food market, are a major cause of Third World starvation.

I do not hold the arguments put out by the purveyors of conventional wisdom to be self-evident: in this book I set out the facts against them. In stating my case I have started close to home, with British agriculture, which I know intimately as a farmer, as a Member of Parliament for a farming constituency, and as a writer on farming and farm policy. A lot can be learned from the British experience of farming. We have here an agriculture that is fairly typical of the more prosperous parts of the world. It is supported by massive quantities of government money, which has led to a steady growth in output, but only at great cost. Publicly, we hear a great deal about the growth in output but, until recently, very little about the cost. The British farmer, that symbol of rugged independence, is now – I hate to say – far more of a charge on the state than a worker in any of the ailing, government-subsidised shipyards or car factories or docks which we hear so much about.

What are the ordinary British consumers and taxpayers getting for this vast government expenditure on agriculture? First, they are getting very expensive food. Secondly, they are getting a national economy that suffers from the diversion of large amounts of capital into agriculture. If such capital were used instead to build industries that genuinely created wealth, and not just consumed it, then the average consumer and taxpayer would find himself and herself living in a more prosperous country, with more jobs and more opportunities for a better life.

Aha, say the purveyors of conventional wisdom: if we spend less on agriculture we will produce less food and have to import more, thus harming our balance of payments. This is untrue for two reasons. The argument can first be weakened by pointing out, as I have done at length in this book, that British agriculture today is itself highly dependent upon imports to maintain its present level of production: fuel, fertiliser, and fodder must be imported to keep the system going. Secondly, the balance of payments argument can be shot down by pointing out that it is based upon a shaky grasp of economic realities. Goods produced at unprofitable cost in this country do not become profitable just because they are sold beyond our shores. The case that can be made for subsidising domestic industries is a social rather than an economic one: it is a way of preserving jobs and local communities, not a way of creating wealth. Money can, and probably should, be spent on preserving rural Britain, but this should not be confused with profitable farming.

Britain is not, of course, alone in forcing up agricultural production at high cost: it is done throughout the Common Market. Britain, as a member state, is part of a system, the Common Agricultural Policy, that is responsible for the notorious 'food mountains' – stockpiles of surplus produce that are stored at vast expense and later dumped in the world market, at even vaster expense, at well below the cost of production.

It is this dumping that damages the agriculture of so many Third World countries. It undermines their efforts to open up export markets of their own, and thus to start generating the wealth that could lead them to industrialisation and a better life. It cannot be emphasised too strongly that malnutrition and starvation in the Third World cannot be blamed on overpopulation or shortage of land, because only about 40 per cent of the arable land in the world is actually under cultivation. Many of the poorest countries have an even smaller percentage of land under cultivation – in the Sudan, for example, it is only 10 per cent. Shortage of food in those countries is a result of poverty, pure and simple.

What the Third World needs if it is to escape from its present poverty is not aid, but trade; and this is where the developed world has failed it. Aid programmes, even the grandiose Lomé Convention between the Common Market and selected Third World countries, only tinker with the problem. What the Third World is asking for is not charity, but a chance to compete on world markets with the commodities and goods that they can produce at economical prices – prices that we, the consumers of the developed world, would be happy to pay.

This we – and they – cannot do under the present system of protectionism and inflated domestic prices. Their loss is our loss. We are deprived of freedom of choice and forced to pay inflated prices due to our government's short-sighted interventionism; they are faced, as a result of this same restriction of freedom, with prospects even more grim. It could be that the long-term prospects are equally grim for us as well.

One could argue for ever over what is the most fundamental division in the world today: that between East and West, between Communism and Capitalism, or that between North and South, wealth and poverty? What should concern us is the fact that the effect of such systems as the Common Agricultural Policy is to make these conflicts one. Third World countries, deprived of markets in the West, may have little choice but to turn to the East. One writer on trade, a New Zealander, once suggested that New Zealand might one day find itself, out of economic necessity, becoming part of the Soviet economic orbit. Almost certainly an exaggeration, but an idea that should make even the most sceptical ponder.

In this book I have estimated the enormous cost of diverting resources – especially capital – to agriculture and away from other industries that would have had those resources but for the intervention of the government in pursuing a policy that artificially expanded agriculture. The other industries, at whose expense this policy has existed, are more efficient than agriculture, in the sense that they are capable of making a profit, out of which they pay taxes to support agriculture, which cannot make a sufficient profit to be a net contributor to the Exchequer. Those industries would have used the resources more efficiently for the wealth of the nation, and the result of diverting them has been a higher level of unemployment and the impoverishment of the nation as a whole.

The farmers, in the main, have not benefited, strange though it may seem, for many thousands of them have had to abandon farming, most of them with the utmost regret and reluctance. The principal beneficiaries have been certain very large companies, such as ICI, Shell, BP and Fisons. In a campaign of remarkable success, they have been at the centre of the argument for protectionism and subsidies, or scorn for 'cheap food' and of the call for agricultural expansion 'in the national interest'. The campaign has been adroit, sophisticated and expensive; yet it has undoubtedly yielded a financial return to those companies that could never have been made without it.

Five arguments have been used: (1) by growing more food we would be 'saving' on the balance of payments; (2) the world's population was increasing so seriously that there would soon be a shortage of food: so long as many millions of the human race were hungry we had a moral duty to grow as much of our own food as possible; (3) we should secure our own supplies of food as we can no longer trust the world market to supply our needs; (4) in the event of another war it would be necessary, for strategic reasons, to be already growing our own food; and (5) an expanded and therefore prosperous agriculture was a means of conserving the countryside.

I do not believe any of these arguments are valid. I have

replied to each of them in a chapter apiece, and I leave it to the reader to judge whether I have succeeded in rebutting them. The onus of establishing the need for the protection of an industry must rest on those who are in its favour. If I have succeeded in showing that their case for protection is no longer valid, the inference is perhaps too obvious for further comment.

This book contains, I hope, a great deal to make the sceptical ponder. It chronicles a system of agricultural support that is expensive, uneconomical, and unjust. It is a system that, for the sake of short term and often illusory gains, is doing untold damage around the world. It cannot be abolished too quickly.

1/Two Sorry Facts

A farm, it is often said, can soak up money as a sponge does hot water. Anyone who has owned even a small farm knows how easy it is to spend limitless sums on improvements, new machinery, modern buildings and better quality livestock. Perfection never comes, because there is always something a little better just around the corner; and usually taxpayers' money in the form of a grant or tax allowance is there to tempt you into having it.

As with individual farms, so with farming as a whole. We can continue, if we wish, to pour hundreds of millions of pounds into the various branches of agriculture – every penny coming from a taxpayer – and still it will be feasible to spend as much again. So far from suggesting the time has come to lessen, still less halt, the flow of taxpayers' money into agriculture, the National Farmers' Union seriously argues that the existing level of support is not enough.

The purpose of this book is to examine whether British agriculture is so incapable of standing on its own feet that it needs to be treated like a lame duck; and if it is lame, does it need a pair of crutches, or a surgical operation?

It is also important to investigate who are the gainers and who the losers in the present system. The figures show that the Treasury is, beyond doubt, a large contributor to the fortunes of agriculture, so every taxpayer is entitled to ask himself whether his money is going in the right direction. Every consumer of food, whose interest is even greater than that of the taxpayer, has a right to know whether the present system interferes with his freedom to choose the food he would like to eat, and also whether he is being called upon to pay a higher price than is necessary. The evidence in this book should convince him that in both respects he is a loser.

Then there is the efficient farmer. I define him as one who is able to earn a livelihood from agriculture – and that includes a proper return on his capital – without being given any subsidy by the Government. If the reader is not persuaded that the efficient farmer is also among the losers then one of my main purposes will have failed. I believe he suffers a greater loss by this system than either the taxpayer or the consumer, for he is the one who has to run in the race with a heavy handicap, against others who would not attempt to compete but for the handicap he has been given. Sadly, he has imbibed the fallacy that his interest is the same as that of his neighbours, even though they cannot match his level of efficiency.

I write as someone who has owned and managed a small farm. For years I have argued the case for a strong and flourishing agriculture. Neither the present Common-Market-based farm policy nor the previous system of national support has provided the foundations for its strength and prosperity in the long term. Unless such long-term objectives are assured, there must come a time when Nemesis will prevail.

The architects of our agricultural policy gloss over two facts that are crucial to the argument. The first is that the great part of the United Kingdom consists of poor quality land, so that attempts to grow food on it can only succeed at very high cost. The second fact, which flows from the first, is that the more we expand British agriculture the more of a lame duck it becomes, needing ever stronger crutches to support it.

Neither fact is palatable to those of us who are proud of what our farmers have achieved. Indeed it would be grossly unfair to disregard the triumph of British agriculture in expanding production to an extent no one would have considered feasible three decades ago; and it would be equally unjust to overlook the way the many scientists, engineers and other technical advisers have assisted in the triumph. In numerous books, newspaper articles and television programmes, the record has been amply chronicled and it does not need to be repeated here.

Yet it has been essentially a technical achievement: science and technology have been applied to agriculture, and the results have been triumphant. Sadly, it has been done at very high cost; and the cost is shameful. There are many thousands of people who have, over the years, succumbed to the special pleading of the agricultural lobby (a term that includes the great industrial companies that have been major beneficiaries) and who will find it difficult to accept that the triumph has been accompanied by such shameful consequences. So it may be useful to examine in some detail these two unpalatable facts.

The total amount of land farmed in the United Kingdom, including rough grazing, is 46,000,000 acres. Looking at this in terms of quality, we find that only 7,800,000 of these acres – 17.4 per cent – is really suitable for the growing of all arable crops. They fall, in other words, into what is known as Grade I and Grade II land.* Yet in our country today over 17 million acres – more than 37 per cent of farm land – are given over to arable farming. It follows that millions of these acres are of Grade III, defined by the Ministry as 'land of average quality', which may yield quite well, perhaps over two tons of wheat to the acre – but only at very high cost. In fact, some simple arithmetic shows that about 9,000,000 acres of Grade III land are now given over to growing arable crops. Those acres represent one fifth of all our agricultural land. (The Minister's intention to reclassify Grade III land is considered in Appendix 1.)

This high-cost farming is possible because a high tax is imposed on wheat and other grains entering this country. The tax, in the form of a variable levy, may change from month to month, but on 30 July 1982 it was £73.48 a metric tonne; and as the price of US wheat was then £73.50 it adds 99 per cent to its price. Shades of the Corn Laws! Not even they, at their most

---

* The Minister of Agriculture gave the following answer to a Written Question about the grades of agricultural land:

Agricultural land in England and Wales is currently classified in 5 grades according to the degree to which certain physical characteristics impose long-term limitations on agricultural use.

Grade I	land of exceptional quality	2.8% of the total
Grade II	land of high quality	14.6% of the total
Grade III	valuable land for a wide range of uses	48.9% of the total
Grade IV	land of restricted potential	19.7% of the total
Grade V	land of very restricted potential	14.0% of the total

(Hansard, 12 November 1980.)

3

oppressive period, ever taxed our wheat half so much as that.

Without these very high taxes imposed upon low-cost imports, it would just not be economic to attempt arable farming on this poorer land. The growing of wheat and other grains would remain predominantly in East Anglia, where suitable land is to be found and where the farmers need fear no competition from abroad.

So the first unpalatable fact is that the quantity of our land that can grow arable crops at an economic price is limited, and our existing arable land is more than double that limit. Most of it should revert to grass and to livestock farming. The latter has become less profitable than it need because all feeding stuffs – the concentrates that are necessary to supplement grass – have become artificially expensive.

'Up corn, down horn' is an old saying; when the growing of corn becomes more profitable, the return on keeping cattle and other stock goes down. That is what is happening today. The levy on maize is almost as high as it is on wheat, £66.17 on 30 July 1982. In percentage terms it is even more oppressive; it adds no less than 117 per cent to its price. As cereals such as wheat or maize form the greater part of the compound, the obvious truth is that artificially supported arable farming has undermined the profitability of the livestock sector, which historically has always been the largest branch of British agriculture. In the process, many thousands of farmers have been driven out of business. One statistic highlights the exodus: in 1964 there were 250,000 farmers with less than a hundred acres, on which, not so long ago, a reasonable livelihood could be made with livestock. Now there are 120,000, and the number falls year after year. When about 70 per cent of the expenditure of a typical pig or poultry farmer is likely to be on feeding compounds, it becomes, needless to say, rather difficult to balance the books.

It is true that the process of artificially stimulating arable farming on Grade III land did not begin with the introduction of import levies. It began when other forms of Government support were given, such as guaranteed prices, grants, subsidies, and tax allowances. But the effect was the same. High-cost farming on unsuitable land was made marginally profitable. It was done at the expense of the taxpayers, importers, consumers and, above all, livestock farmers. The enterprises of the latter became, as each year went by, marginally more unprofitable. As the profitability of arable farming increased artificially, year by year, so the profitability of livestock farming decreased artificially. If successive Governments had not intervened, arable farming would not have expanded and livestock farmers would not have been forced out of business. The latter survived by being forced into ever fewer and ever larger units. In 1950 a dairy farmer could earn a living with 15 cows; now, to earn the same income in real terms, he needs 75. He has gained nothing, except the worry of having to find ever more capital. Is he more efficient? It depends what one means by the term. In later chapters I will argue that productivity is not the yardstick to adopt. The transfer of resources to agriculture, especially capital, has not been 'efficient'. It has reduced the economic well-being of the British people. It has caused other industries to be more heavily taxed than they would otherwise have been; it has diverted capital away from them, and it has aggravated the evil of unemployment.

The main burden of supporting agriculture now falls on the consumer who indirectly pays the taxes on imported food. Before we went over to the system of import levies and intervention buying, the cost was borne by the taxpayers. The distinction is important at a time of recession and high unemployment because millions of consumers are on, near or below the poverty line, and a considerable part of the cost of supporting agriculture falls upon them rather than on those who can afford to do so. Which brings us to the second unpalatable fact: that farmers have received such massive sums of money from the public that they far outweigh the largesse given to any other of our industries. From 1953 until we entered the EEC, 45 to 80 per cent of the farmer's income came out of the pocket of the taxpayer; now it is over 100 per cent. Given such a high level of subsidy, it is difficult to argue that our agriculture has become 'efficient'. I hope to show that the efficiency of our farming is declining; that is, if the efficiency of an industry is measured by the degree of support it needs.

Those who defended the old system of support used to claim that it had the effect of reducing food prices, so it was in fact a subsidy for the consumer and not the farmer. It was a claim that was really quite untrue. The system of support took different forms, but whatever form it was in, it never operated unless home-produced food was more expensive than the imported variety. It always acted in a way that displaced imports. Thus in every case when a customer bought home-produced food that had its price influenced by Government support, it would have been possible for him to have bought the same kind of food from abroad at an equal or even lower price.

In other words, the support system gave no advantage to the consumer. The beneficiary was intended to be the farmer, but not every farmer benefited from the system. On the contrary, I believe that it has been to the detriment of many tens of thousands of them. A system of grants and subsidies serves no purpose at all unless it distorts the price mechanism; and the only way to ensure that the naturally efficient producer receives the highest return is to allow the price mechanism to equate supply and demand.

Table I spells out the extent to which British agriculture has been supported. Column 3 is the one that deserves particular study. It shows that in 1955-56 58.9 per cent of farmers' income was attributable to Exchequer support. In 1970-71 it was 42 per cent and in the intervening period it reached a peak of 80.5 per cent. The average was 61.6 per cent: a disturbingly high proportion of farmers' incomes.

In subsequent years it will be seen that the percentages fell quite considerably. The reason is the change-over from the old system of deficiency payments and guaranteed prices to a system of import levies in preparation for our entry into the EEC in 1973.

The old system of support enabled the taxpayer to know exactly how much of his money was going to the farmers. Now, and ever since 1971, the truth must be sought beneath a shroud of camouflage. One of the arguments advanced to the farmers for the new system was that it would bring to an end the annual tug-of-war between the Treasury and the Ministry of Agriculture over how much support should be given. Being

Table I: The Cost of Exchequer Support

	Farmers' net income £ million	UK Exchequer cost of agricultural support £ million	Agricultural support as % of farming net income
1955-56	350	206	58.9
1956-57	340½	239	70.2
1957-58	376	284	75.5
1958-59	332½	241	72.5
1959-60	362½	257	70.9
1960-61	392	263	67.1
1961-62	426	343	80.5
1962-63	447½	310	69.3
1963-64	409½	295	72.0
1964-65	477	264	55.3
1965-66	464½	238	51.2
1966-67	483	229	47.4
1967-68	516½	261	50.5
1968-69	480½	265	55.2
1969-70	568	268	47.2
1970-71	610	256	42.0
1971-72	706	201	28.5
1972-73	832	191	23.0
1973-74	1,283	193	15.0
1974-75	1,263	289	22.9
1975-76	1,676	191	11.4
1976-77	1,751	208	11.9
1977-78	1,301	198	15.2
1978-79	1,263	185	14.6
1979-80	1,145	300	26.2
1980-81	1,162	358	30.8

Note

1955-56 is taken as the first year because in previous years a substantial part of the cost of agricultural support was subsumed in the trading losses of the Ministry of Food and thus cannot be separately identified.

The principal source for Table 2 has been the Annual Reviews, and the farmers' income figures are as defined there. Both those and the Exchequer support figures in column 2 are liable to revision in subsequent Annual Reviews.

myself an advocate of the change at that time, I went so far as to publish a booklet showing that with import duties on food the two Departments would acquire a common interest in maintaining them at a high level. When import duties or levies are imposed upon food from abroad, it is extremely difficult to calculate just what effect they are having upon prices; and consumers are left in the dark as to how much more they are paying for their food. But whether called levies, duties or tariffs, they still remain a form of taxation. Under the present system, everyone who eats food becomes a taxpayer, yet he is unlikely to be conscious of the fact, and certainly not aware of the precise amount he is paying in this form of taxation in order to support agriculture.

The new system of support had a happy effect upon farmers' incomes. In two years they leapt up by no less than 100 per cent and in the next two years rose by another one third. As the new system coincided with various experiments by the Government to control incomes, perhaps it might not be altogether churlish to note that the new system of state control to increase farmers' incomes enabled them to enjoy a very much higher rise in income than was ordained by two successive Governments in their incomes' policies for the rest of the British people.

Table I must, therefore, be revised for the years since the truth about agricultural support has been concealed from the taxpayer by the operation of the Common Agricultural Policy. Although it is extremely difficult to ascertain the extent to which taxpayers' money is being diverted into the farmer's pocket, the Institute for Fiscal Studies has done some interesting research in this field. For the purpose of this book, they have provided Table II, which gives a truer picture of the degree of support afforded to British farmers as a result of the new system. The columns setting out farmers' net income and the UK Exchequer support are the same as in Table I. The column headed 'Price support' is the value to the farmer of the system of import duties and levies imposed by the CAP. The two forms of support are added together each year to form a separate column to indicate the overall support agriculture received from the taxpayer. The final column shows how much of the farmer's income is derived from the taxpayer.

Table II: The cost overall of taxpayers' support (£ million)

	Farmers' net income	'Price support'	Exchequer support	Overall taxpayers' support	Taxpayers' support as % of farmers' net income
1971/72	706	210	201	411	58
1972/73	832	204	191	395	47
1973/74	1,283	96	193	289	23
1974/75	1,263	109	289	398	32
1975/76	1,676	512	191	703	42
1976/77	1,751	531	208	739	42
1977/78	1,301	863	198	1061	82
1978/79	1,263	1144	185	1329	105
1979/80	1,145		300		
1980/81	1,162	1570	358	1928	166

As readers may have some difficulty in believing figures that portray a lame duck so grotesquely deformed, Appendix 2 explains the complex method by which the enormous sum of price support was calculated. It is an edited extract from an article by Mr C. N. Morris, the senior research officer of the Institute for Fiscal Studies, that appeared in its journal, *Fiscal Studies*, in March 1980. It is believed the article was read by certain officials in the Treasury with incredulity, so they submitted it to a critical scrutiny which confirmed its truth.

Three particular comments need to be made about Table II. The first is that in the years 1973/74 and 1974/75 farmers received support that was less than one third of their income. This was considerably less than usual because world prices for wheat and sugar temporarily rose and were higher than EEC prices. In a subsequent chapter the reasons for this phenomenon are given, and no one seriously argues that they are ever likely to recur. In fact, if we were to adopt a free trade policy, it would be unthinkable for world prices to become higher than those of the EEC, as the later chapter shows. The years 1975/76 and 1976/77, when farmers' support was 42 per cent, were a time when the world's producers of wheat and sugar were recovering from the turmoil; and by 1977/78 they had recovered.

Secondly, Table II demonstrates a rising trend. 82 per cent is followed by 105 per cent and then 166 per cent. All the evidence indicates that this rising trend must continue. The reason is that food consumption in the EEC remains constant or, so far as several items are concerned, is tending to go down, yet food production is going up. As the surpluses have to be dumped onto the world market, world prices become depressed, and the more they are depressed, the more money is needed by Brussels for the guarantee section of the CAP funds, so the higher the figure in column 2 becomes.

The rising trend was confirmed by Mr Christopher Tugendhat, the Vice President of the EEC Commission, when he addressed the annual meeting of the British Association for the Advancement of Science on 7 September 1982. He said that were Britain to replace the support given to farmers under the CAP with a system of deficiency payments, it would cost the taxpayer about £2,000 millions (the figure he would insert in column 2 for the current year). The Annual Review for 1982 forecasts that national grants and subsidies for 1981/82 will cost £269 millions, so the overall taxpayers' support will be £2,269 millions. The latest forecast for farmers' income is £1,209 millions. Thus, according to Mr Tugendhat, the overall cost of taxpayers' support is now 188% of farmers' income.

However, statistics prepared by the Commission for its spokesmen are not necessarily reliable and they tend to be tailored for public consumption rather than serious argument; and in this case Mr Tugendhat was trying to prove that a return to deficiency payments would be very expensive for the British taxpayer. In doing so, he was guilty of a fallacy obvious to anyone who is more familiar with British agriculture. He failed to appreciate that the pattern of farming would change very considerably if we were to return to deficiency payments. The millers and livestock producers would again be able to buy their cereals from abroad, so the emphasis would move from high-cost cereal growing to the naturally more economic livestock production. The total cost of support would then diminish; and, as a percentage of farming income, it would be likely to fall from the present 166% to the average that existed when we had deficiency payments, about 62%. Assuming farmers' incomes remain the same, price support would therefore be about £481 millions instead of Mr Tugendhat's figure of four times as much.

However, Mr Tugendhat's fallacy does not detract from the essential theme. Price support afforded by the CAP will have to increase in 1982. The EEC Commission expects record surpluses of cereals and dairy produce, which will have to be exported with the aid of subsidies larger than ever before. Its officials have been reported as saying that the £7,700 millions so far allocated to the CAP will not be enough for the purpose. Mr Tugendhat's 188%, then, seems likely to be an underestimate for the future.

The third and final comment is this: Table II highlights an absurdity. There may be plenty of taxpayers anxious to pay for some part of the farmers' income; some may even be willing to pay all his income. But paying 66% more than his income for the purpose of giving him financial support seems to be taking generosity to the point of absurdity. 166% may seem impossible. But the impossible is what we are asking British agriculture to do. We are asking it to produce ever more of our food at a price we can afford, and that it simply cannot do.

To grow bananas on the side of Ben Nevis would be totally absurd, but technically it could be done; and no doubt if it were achieved, it would be hailed as a triumph. The earth on the slopes of Ben Nevis, such as it is, would have to be considerably improved, probably many tons of good soil dragged up and then heavily fertilised. Huge glasshouses would be necessary and constructed with elaborate support to withstand storms and snow, and then heated to an inordinate degree. Special varieties of bananas would have to be evolved. And it would all cost vast sums of money. No one in their right mind would spend their own savings on such foolery, but it is not beyond the realms of probability to find others who would be willing to learn the skills if offered enough public money to do so. When the bananas came to be sold the economic price might be £3 or £4 each, and then the special pleading would begin. 'Buy British,' we would be told; every pound spent on a home-grown banana is a pound saved on the balance of payments. We need 'secure supplies' of bananas and we cannot be sure that Jamaica or the Windward Islands would continue to supply us with 'essential fruits' in a hostile world. 'The Banana Industry of Ben Nevis is needed to provide jobs for Highlanders who would otherwise be out of work.' The NFU would call for a massive injection of fresh capital to enable this valuable new industry to reach its full potential; and in the columns of the farming press it would all be written up, with bated breath, as 'a triumph for Britain'.

Absurdity is only a matter of degree. Not so very far down the scale is the growing of wheat on what was, a few years ago, the heather-strewn moorland of North Yorkshire. A banana grown on the slopes of Ben Nevis might cost fifty times more than one in Jamaica; a ton of wheat in North Yorkshire, about three times more than one in Manitoba; and both are the fruits of absurdity.

Come the day when the Minister of Agriculture and the NFU achieve their ambition of total self-sufficiency, the percentage in the last column of Table II will be a great deal higher still. If bananas are singled out as a separate item, it could be any crazy figure – 1,000 per cent or more. On the other hand, if British agriculture produced the food which it can do competitively, the percentage would fall to zero.

Let us suppose we are out of the Mad Hatter's world and once more our farmers are treated by the British public as efficient producers of some of – but not all – our needs. Milk is one of them, and we are undoubtedly very competent in dairy farming. If there were then no import levies on cereals, the compound feeding stuffs, which represent a high proportion of the dairy farmers' total costs, could well fall to nearly half their present price. Once these levies were removed, our dairy farmers would be given such a boost to their income that any support from the taxpayer would become totally unnecessary. In one word, their percentage support in the last column of Table II would be – nil. The same can be said for a number of others, particularly pig and egg producers.

If a Table II were constructed for the years before World War II, there would be virtually a blank, just empty columns except for modest sums under Exchequer Support and 1 per cent or less in the final column with monotonous regularity for every year. Towards the end of this book an attempt is made to put those pre-war farming years in a more accurate light than the accepted wisdom permits. Times were difficult for farmers then (and I can submit my own anecdotal evidence as well as anyone), but so they were for everyone in our country. No amount of special pleading can disguise the fact that when taxpayers' support accounted for less than 1 per cent of farmers' income, there were hundreds of thousands more families able to earn a livelihood on the land than is the case today.

Table II illustrates that overall taxpayers' support is now £1934 millions, but it is the total of just two kinds of support. It is by no means the end of the story. In the next chapter there is a catalogue of the other items: they add up to billions of pounds.

Now if all this transfer of wealth were enabling many thousands of small farmers to remain on the land, to care for it as trustees of the future, and provide us with wholesome food which we would be otherwise unlikely to eat, there might be some kind of justification for the gigantic scale of this transfer of resources. That is patently not the case. A major argument against the present system is that the small farmer is being driven out, and the large farmer is becoming larger.

As the Minister's Annual Review of Agriculture, 1982, puts it:

The decline in the number of farms in the United Kingdom continues. . . . The fall in numbers continued to be greatest among the smaller full-time businesses.

The Review tells us that in 1981 the total number of holdings was about 242,300. The corresponding figure for 1953 was 454,000. Overwhelmingly, the exit of those 211,000 has been among smaller farmers. To dismiss them as 'unviable' would be a cruel calumny; it would be nearer the truth to say they were made unprofitable by the way the support system has been operated. It has been the policy of successive Governments since 1953 to encourage farm amalgamations, and the encouragement has been provided by a whole range of grants and tax allowances being tilted in favour of the large farmer.

As a broad generalisation, the smaller farmer tended to be dependant on livestock and the larger farmer upon arable crops. What has happened over most of England is that the small livestock holdings that were predominantly given over to

13

pasture have been amalgamated into substantial farms, and the pasture ploughed up to grow corn. These farms are generally owner-occupied rather than tenanted, and so the typical farmer of today is likely to possess assets worth half a million pounds and to employ only one or two men. He may have borrowed heavily from the bank, but he remains a rich man, having become probably twice as well off in terms of both capital and income. But it should not be overlooked that most new entrants to farming in recent years have not been young men beginning their career with limited resources. The opportunities that used to be theirs are lost – destroyed by the present system. Instead, when a farm of any substantial size comes onto the market, it is likely to be sold to a middle-aged man who has made his money in some other walk of life. Is this really to the advantage of farming? Perhaps it is time for the leaders of the NFU to pause a while and to contemplate what the future holds should this process continue much longer.

The alternative policy that I describe in a subsequent chapter will not make it tougher for farming. It may indeed be tougher for those who have benefited from ploughing up pasture to grow wheat at inordinate cost, but not for arable farmers with Grade I and II land, and certainly not for the many thousands of young men and women who would like to have a small farm of their own, doing what the small farmer can do best – producing livestock.

It is true that there are livestock farmers, especially in Scotland, Wales and the upland parts of England, who have survived upon marginal land, Grade IV and V – and who would not have done so without some kind of support from the taxpayer. The countryside would be, and look, the poorer for their departure from the land. Their problem prompts two thoughts. In the first place, there is an alternative policy which would give them the assistance they need and which the taxpayer might be unlikely to resent. In a word, it would mean paying them to farm as custodians of the countryside, and I have set out some details of it in the subsequent chapter entitled 'Conserving the Countryside'.

Secondly, before we get too sentimental about the farmer having to sell up and abandon a home as well as a job, we might

14

spare a thought for all the many thousands of others who have suffered that fate in the last two or three decades; and each one of them concerned with the business of feeding others. I have in mind all those small (and some not so small) grocers, butchers, bakers, greengrocers and others who managed to earn a livelihood before, during and immediately after the War. In many cases they were family businesses, inherited, and above the shop was the family home. There cannot be a town in our country of any size where thirty or forty of them have not gone to the wall. Incidentally, the grocer's shop owned by Mrs Thatcher's father in Grantham falls precisely into this category; today it stands forlornly empty. The part all these many tens of thousands of shops played in supplying food to the nation was just as important economically as that of the farmers of marginal land. In fact they were more important: the hill farmers in the main were producing high-cost lamb and beef both of which were readily available from other countries at about half the price; and while they called for ever more subsidies, a whole legion of shopkeepers went to the wall without once daring to echo the same cry for help.

The massive sums of money set out in the Table can be seen in the account of the nation. They are visible. They can be scrutinised and mulled over, debated and discussed; the House of Commons can vote on them, and we can all pass judgment on whether or not they should be paid. However, there is also an unseen, invisible payment in both cash and kind that has to be made as a result of the policy of expanding an industry as large as agriculture from the size it would have been but for Government intervention to the size it has become. This unseen payment is so huge that it makes the Treasury subsidy to agriculture look like the proverbial chicken feed. It flows from the diversion of resources caused by enlarging one industry to about twice the size it would otherwise be at the expense of every other industry. The effects upon the wealth of our nation are so great that they deserve three fresh Chapters, to consider in turn the diversion of capital, of land use, of labour, and of natural resources such as fuel and fertilisers. There is also the grievous effect it is having upon the lifeblood of our nation – trade – and this wider issue is examined in Chapter 8.

The True Cost of
Supporting Agriculture

2/The Diversion of Capital

The diversion of capital to agriculture by the government is incalculable. By any test it is enormous, but the difficulty lies in assessing how great is the enormity. However, there can be no argument about one point: the diversion of capital must be from other branches of our trade or industry that would have been able to hold on to their capital but for interference by the government. Capital flows naturally to those trades and industries which can offer the highest interest, and that must be those that are the most profitable. Profitability is, as a general rule, a measure of commercial popularity, because profits go to those who give the public what it wants. Of course, there are exceptions, but they are usually created by some intervention into the normal price mechanism. Of that there is no better example than the way property companies have made inordinate profits in recent years, as a result of the Rent Acts and planning controls. Now, if profits are an indicator of what the public prefers – a kind of popularity poll – it seems to be flying in the face of what the public wants for the state to step in and use its powers to transfer capital to some other branch of industry.

Some of this capital that has been transferred to agriculture is the taxpayer's money, but it may be the smallest part of the total. Table I in chapter 1 sets out the grants and subsidies received by farmers since 1953. The total comes to £7,477,000,000. It is not, however, the full cost to the taxpayer of supporting agriculture: we must also take into account the expenditure incurred by the Ministry in administering the subsidies. We must also consider the functions of the Ministry itself. To what extent would we need a Ministry of Agriculture at all if it were not for the policy of support? There is no need for a Ministry for Clothing. Nor do we have a Ministry for the

19

Chemical Industry, nor a Ministry for Butchers, Grocers, or even the whole Retail Trade. We do indeed have a state that interferes with them all, but the existing Departments of Trade, Industry and Consumer Protection seem to suffice.

In terms of expenditure and staff, the Ministry of Agriculture has been one of the largest in the post-war era. Steadily, it has increased the amount of public money it has spent. In 1938, at a time when there were twice as many farms as today, when 950,000 people were employed on the land, and when agriculture, especially in the livestock sector, was expanding rapidly and profitably (as shown in a later chapter), gross expenditure by the Ministry of Agriculture & Fisheries was a mere £3,985,654 – £8 per farmer! The pound, we all know, has since fallen to one-fifteenth of its 1938 value, so in 1982 terms that gross expenditure would be £60,000,000. Looking at the 1981-82 Estimates for the Ministry of Agriculture, we see that Parliament has approved the sum of £753,766,000 for its gross expenditure. This is more than a twelve-fold increase on the 1938 Estimates, after making full allowance for the fall in the value of the pound. And this does not include the main support which agriculture receives from the operation of import duties and import levies under the Common Agricultural Policy. Nor does it take into account the numerous other kinds of financial assistance given to agriculture that we shall look at later.

The Estimates are but a starting point in examining the way our system of taxation is diverting capital to agriculture from other industries. As the effect upon industry is cumulative, it is essential for the purpose of the argument to see how much has been diverted in this way since the War. Adding up the Estimates since 1946 one reaches a total of £14,000,000,000, but in terms of the present value of the pound the total would be some £40,000,000,000.

As the number of farms becomes fewer and their sizes larger, the greater the degree of support they seem to need. This seems to be contrary to what we have been induced to believe about the necessity of making farms 'viable' with public money.

This is well borne out in the reply by the Prime Minister to a Written Question, set out in Hansard, 12 November 1981, Column 164. She was asked to state the percentage increases or decreases in expenditure since 1979 in real terms of each of the seventeen programmes of public expenditure. Her reply contained the following table:

	Programme	Change per cent
1	Defence	+ 4.9
2	Overseas Aid and other Overseas Services	−20.3
3	Agriculture, Fisheries, Food and Forestry	+13.9
4	Industry, Energy, Trade and Employment	+33.1
5	Government Lending to Nationalised Industries	+10.4
6	Transport	− 4.8
7	Housing	−13.6
8	Other Environmental Services	− 4.5
9	Law, Order and Protective Services	+ 5.0
10	Education and Science, Arts and Libraries	− 3.5
11	Health and Personal Social Services	+ 0.7
12	Social Security	+ 3.5
13	Other Public Services	+ 1.1
14	Common Services	+ 0.3
15	Scotland	− 2.9
16	Wales	− 2.9
17	Northern Ireland	+ 1.4
	Planning Total	+ 1.9

The figures really speak for themselves. Nevertheless, the significance of agriculture being the second largest gainer must not be overlooked; its percentage increase of 13.9 can be compared with the percentage decreases accorded to transport, housing and education.

In going through the Estimates, one finds that there are benefits going to agriculture, other than in cash, which nonetheless cost money to provide. Perhaps the most important is ADAS. This is the Agricultural Development Advisory Service, the successor to the National Agricultural Advisory Service. It provides a service that is free to the farmer, yet it now costs no less than £52,000,000 a year in salaries alone, and a further £9,000,000 in travelling expenses. Members of its staff are, in effect, the business and technical consultants to any farmer who wants advice; and there are no less than 4,706 of them. It is noteworthy that there are only a very few consultants in private practice, despite agriculture being an industry whose methods are constantly changing and one in which the expertise demanded of most farmers is increasing year by year. Why pay a £200 fee when you can get the services of a consultant for nothing – and a consultant supported by a massive team of research workers? ADAS is in fact a nationalised service: it is the nationalisation of the agricultural consultants' profession.

Agricultural research paid for by the Ministry is another large item. It is now costing about £70,000,000 a year. Every facet of agriculture comes within this ambit and some notable advances have been made in animal health, plant breeding, and other fields. The results are made available to the farmer through ADAS and the farming press. No other industry is supported by so much free research – free to the customer, that is – and a consultancy service on such a scale.

Much of the research is undertaken at our universities, but only about £500,000 of the £70,000,000 in the Agriculture Estimates is accounted for in this way. The rest of the cost is borne by another set of Estimates, those of the Department of Education and Science. It is quite impossible to disentangle from the Education Estimates just how much goes indirectly into supporting agriculture, but sixteen of our universities own or rent farms for purposes other than an investment*. They add up to 13,844 acres and must be worth not less than £20,000,000. Frequently the farming press will report the results of what they have achieved, and it is thus passed on to the farmer to his advantage. While it is impossible to calculate the total cost to the taxpayer of this share of the Education Estimates, it goes a long way to set off those items in the Agriculture Estimates that are manifestly not spent in the interests of our farmers, such as the subscription to the International Coffee Organisation (£51,137) or to the International Cocoa Organisation (£33,500) or even the World Rabbit Association (£25).

Then there is the Agricultural Training Board. In every other industry, employers are required by law to pay a levy to help the appropriate training board meet the costs of training employees. Not so agriculture. Under the original legislation

* Answer to a Parliamentary Question: House of Commons, 7 March 1978.

22

that was passed, farmers were placed on the same basis as any other group of employers, but they fought a determined campaign against it and eventually it had to be changed to afford them their present privilege. (I am certainly not complaining about this, for I myself played as vigorous a part as any in the campaign. But I had hoped that employers in other industries who trained their own employees would also fight the extravagant bureaucracy of these training boards.) According to the current report of the Agricultural Training Board, it proposes to spend £7,600,000 in the current year. To what extent this really is in the interests of farmers, there may be room for doubt, but the Board's expenditure this year does include £1,214,000 as 'grants to employers', a modest enough gift horse, not to be refused.

A great deal more to the point are the tax advantages that have gradually been made available to farmers; not to all of them, but to certain categories, and none more so than those who own their land or farm on a large scale.

First of all, the cost of buying nearly every kind of implement or machine used on the farm can be written off against income tax in one year. The larger and more prosperous the farmer, the greater is this benefit. Every large-scale cereal grower, having made substantial profits in recent years, has purchased many thousands of pounds' worth of new machinery and has had most of it paid for him by the tax inspector. If such a farmer has an income of over £30,000 – a gross income that size is to be expected if the farm is over 500 acres – income tax would ordinarily take substantially more than half of that away from him. By purchasing new machinery to that amount, he thus gains a very happy advantage! The Annual Review of Agriculture publishes the expenditure on new plant machinery and buildings; assuming that farmers are paying tax at the standard rate, this assistance costs the Exchequer some £700,000,000 a year.

There can be no doubt that this tax advantage has stimulated the sales of tractors, combines and most forms of machinery. In doing so it has probably forced up the price of some of them. Experts in the trade say that quite ordinary tractors may cost £8,000 compared with £1,000 for a comparable model some years ago, which is an increase of approximately double that of motor cars or other commercial vehicles. If this has been the result of the tax advantage it has borne very severely upon the small farmer who does not earn enough to set off the cost of a new tractor against his income tax. The fact is that very few small farmers are now able to afford a new tractor or other machinery at the present prices; and new entrants to farming find it impossible, unless they come in as rich men.

Another benefit is exemption from VAT. The Ministry of Agriculture in its evidence to the House of Commons Select Committee on Agriculture estimated it to be worth £300,000,000 a year to farmers. Parliament has also made considerable concessions under the Capital Transfer Tax. All small businesses are entitled to CTT relief; but agriculture is placed in a more favourable position still, provided the farm does not exceed 1,000 acres. Even that proviso can nonetheless be avoided by a husband and wife dividing between themselves a holding of 2,000 acres or taking in a third partner in the form of a charitable trust to extend the privilege to a 3,000 acre estate. Mr Alister Sutherland of Cambridge University, when Special Adviser to the Northfield Committee on Land Ownership, made a most valuable study on this subject and a summary of it was published in *Fiscal Studies* (volume 1, no. 2). One of the points that emerge is that the owner of a farm of 500 acres, worth nearly £1,000,000, can avoid CTT altogether by means of a number of quite simple steps which would include taking out an insurance policy costing 40 pence an acre. Tax planners have feasted themselves upon the intricacies of CTT and there is no doubt that they all with one accord encourage their clients, if they are rich enough, to take advantage of being a farmer. Ideally, a very rich businessman should abandon his company and start a new career as a 'full-time farmer' in the latter part of his middle age and his children should then be able to inherit nearly all his wealth without being irritated by the tax inspector.

But how much revenue is being lost in this way; and how much more revenue must be raised from other sources as a result? I asked the Chancellor of the Exchequer for an estimate of this loss and, in his reply, it was calculated that if farmers were treated the same as ordinary small businessmen, they would have been liable for another £3 million in the fiscal year of 1980/81, and a further £20 million were they treated as other people (Hansard, 17 June 1981). As Capital Transfer Tax would not affect most tenant farmers (who are approximately half the total), this is a considerable sum to be divided among the limited numbers of large farmers who either died or happened to transfer their land *inter vivos* in just one year.

These privileges under the present system of Capital Transfer Tax are of little or no benefit to the small farmer or the tenant. As they probably have the effect of artificially increasing the value of land, it is arguable that his opportunity of acquiring a larger holding or buying his farm is diminished. Certainly they place his large scale competitor in a more favourable position than himself, and to that extent they create an element of unfair competition. By any criterion they are unjust, socially and economically.

Then there is the delicate subject of rate relief. Farm land itself has never been rated, unlike in Ireland where they have the opposite system to ours – domestic houses are exempt but land is charged. Legislation was passed a few years ago to give all farmers relief from rates on buildings and this included the so-called factory farms. The dividing line lacks any logic. If a poultry producer slaughters his stock on the premises, the building maintained for the purpose is exempt, but if his stock is taken down the road to a poultry slaughterhouse, it is not. This exemption from rates is worth £200,000,000 to the farmers (Evidence of the Ministry of Agriculture to the House of Commons Select Committee on Agriculture, April 1982).

Finally, there is a tax privilege that goes back some fifty years. Farmers are entitled to repayment of the excise duty on fuel oil. This is 0.77 pence per litre on oil other than kerosene and 0.22 pence per litre on kerosene. Although the Treasury loses only £3,000,000 a year as a result, it is nonetheless some indication of the vast quantities of oil that are used up by agriculture.

It is by means such as these that farmers pay only 15 per cent of their income in tax. The Minister of State at the Treasury has revealed to the House of Commons that the proportion of their income paid in tax is the same as the farmworker (Hansard, 11

November 1980 Column 161). The latter is among the lowest of the low paid. The Low Pay Unit has defined 'low pay' as earnings less than £75 a week; and the Government considers a two-child family with an income of less than £74 a week is poor enough to be entitled to Family Income Supplement. In a paper published by the Low Pay Unit in January 1981, entitled 'Sowing the Seeds of Discontent', it shows that one in eight full-time manual workers were in that category in April, 1980, but among farm workers the figure was three times the average, being 35.5 per cent.

Families in receipt of the Family Income Supplement are also able to claim free school meals, free welfare milk and rent and rate rebates. While farmworkers are manifestly among the worst paid, on those figures, the system of tax allowances enables their employers to submit revenue returns that place them in the same category, since both pay the same proportion of their income in tax.

We now come to the most grievous and damaging item. It is £1,500,000,000, the cost of 'price support' calculated by the IFS and set out in Table II. The Minister of Agriculture has given it as twice that amount in answer to a Written Question. This is the sum total of the extra cost for food that the consumers in our country must pay: the difference between the prices they pay and the prices they would pay if they were able to buy on the world market. Now it is frequently said that were we to re-enter the world market for our food, the extra demand would force up prices, so there can be no guarantee that we would be able to buy what we needed at existing world prices. In a subsequent chapter this point is answered in some detail, but as it goes to the root of the argument, a summary might be usefully rehearsed. While it is obvious an increased demand for a limited supply of any kind of food will cause its price to rise, it should be equally plain that resources exist in the world to increase food production. Once it was known that 0.8 per cent of the world's population had been set free to buy from the remaining 99.2 per cent, it is inconceivable that the statistically tiny increase in demand could not be met by the millions of farmers in other parts of the world who have the capacity to expand production and would be only too glad to improve their incomes. They would do so in the knowledge that their new customers were able and willing to pay existing world prices, unlike the hundreds of millions in the Third World who now go hungry only because they cannot afford those prices. In fact, world prices would tend to go down for several important commodities, such as wheat and dairy products, once we were no longer bound by the Common Agricultural Policy, because the Continental surpluses that come here now would have to be sold on the world market at even more subsidised prices, and this dumping – like any dumping – would have the effect of forcing down prices.

We can thus assume that we could, if we so wished, buy the food we need at ordinary world prices. The British consumer would be able to spend that extra amount of money on his other needs. The consequent gain to our depressed manufacturing industries could be quite considerable. The import duties and import levies imposed upon so much of what we eat are a form of hidden taxation; and it is taxation to the extent of £1,500,000,000.

We are now able to add up the sums of public money that go to support agriculture. To the £1,500,000,000 must be added the tax privileges that come to about £1,000,000,000, the exemption from rates worth £200,000,000 and the Estimates of the Ministry of Agriculture worth, after excluding items unconnected with agriculture, £650,000,000. Together, they come to £3,350,000,000. This is almost exactly £13,000 for every farmer. As many thousands of small tenant livestock farmers are unable to gain a fair proportion of the benefits, so there must be a much greater gain than the average for those for whom the system works to greater advantage, namely the owner-occupier of a large arable farm. Many of the latter can produce accounts to deny that their incomes have been inflated to such an extent; in doing so they demonstrate a simple truth that underlies the absurd waste of the system. The more uneconomic a business is, the greater the subsidy that is necessary to enable its owner to have an income to live on. Their inability to show a grossly inflated income is a measure of how hopelessly uneconomic their farming would be in the absence of an enormous amount of public money.

Agriculture: The Triumph and the Shame

As the sum of £3,350,000,000 is being diverted each year to agriculture away from where it would otherwise be spent, in effect from other industries and services, it may be instructive to compare it with the capital of some of our greatest companies. It is almost the total capital of our four main clearing banks (£3,546,000,000). It is very much more than the capital of I.C.I. (£1,936,000,000), three times that of Unilever (£1,133,000,000) and thirteen times that of Courtaulds (£245,900,000). To suggest that thirteen new companies the size of Courtaulds could be established every year, were a different policy pursued, cannot be entirely unreasonable.

The total burden, while directly falling upon individual taxpayers and consumers, is one which also has to be borne by the rest of British industry. The effect must be devastating, although it may be a matter for conjecture as to how far we can attribute the recession to the enormous amount of taxation paid by industry as a direct result of these demands upon the Exchequer, or indirectly because of the higher wages made necessary by both costlier food and a higher level of taxation imposed upon its employees.

While it may be obvious that the efficient industries could afford to make this money available, the point needs to be made that they are deprived of spending it as they would have done. Every penny collected by the Chancellor of the Exchequer comes ultimately from industry in some form or another. The more he collects, the less is available for allocation by those who are the managers of industry. It might be an increase in research and development; it might be the building of a new factory; it might be an increase in wages or of dividends; or it might be some other step taken to meet the demands of the public. Whatever the decision by those who have the power to decide, it would have been done to further what the managers considered to be the best interests of their enterprise. Thus any degree of taxation can never add to the strength of an industry or assist its expansion, but must serve to weaken it. That can be questioned only by someone who has good reasons for claiming that the managers of industry are not, as a general rule, capable of making the decisions for which they are employed.

The very prosperous enterprise may, of course, carry its

28

burden of taxation in its stride, but no matter how profitable its business may be, its capacity to remain profitable must be diminished. Its ability to do for the public what the public itself wants it to do must therefore become less. This is what the apologists of state subsidies always overlook. Less prosperous concerns, in paying their share of taxation, fare less well. Many are on the margin of profitability. These are the enterprises, both large and small – and we can all think of the names of some of the very large ones – which have been so weakened by taxation that they have ceased to make any profit at all. If taxation had been, for instance, half of what it has been since the war, would so many household names in industry have gone to the wall? It would be churlish indeed to attribute the fall of all the giants to the cost of supporting agriculture, but it would be equally ridiculous to assert that none has fallen as a result of that extra, perhaps marginal, sum of money transferred from them to agriculture. £3,350,000,000 divided by the number of ultimate taxpayers in industry remains a great deal of money.

The correct way of looking at this figure of over three thousand million pounds is to say that, but for the policy of supporting agriculture, other industries would have had a very large proportion of that money to spend upon their own development and their own expansion. Obviously, no amount of hindsight could describe how such a vast sum would have been spent had it remained with the industries that were then efficient. We cannot even calculate the extent that their efficiency was impaired. Nevertheless, even the most rabid protectionist would have to admit two clear facts. The first is that the industries that paid over those vast sums to the Treasury, directly or indirectly, must have been efficient in the sense that I used that word at the outset. The second is that their capacity to supply the public with what it wants must now be less than it would have been. Anyone who questions this must also deny that taxation in any form has the effect of diverting resources, and especially capital.

The taxation necessary to pay for agricultural support is not the only way by which capital gets diverted from efficient industries to an industry like agriculture which would fail to attract its own capital by the rewards it could offer without government support. In the first place the price of farmland would be markedly less than it is. If the cost of buying good quality, albeit not the best, land was £25 an acre in 1939, it is now about £1,500. Farms that changed hands at £10 per acre before the war are now worth a hundred times more. This phenomenal increase is no less than 10 times more than the rate of inflation! It is not my purpose to argue in favour of a return to all pre-war policies, but if they had continued after 1945, it is arguable that the price of agricultural land would have risen at much the same rate as the pound has depreciated in value. Assuming that the pound has fallen to one fifteenth of its pre-war value, and if £25 an acre was a fair price for goodish land before the war, then it should now be £375. Yet this is £1,125 below the present market price! Multiply that excess value by the number of such acres and another massive figure appears in our balance sheet.

But it is not just those acres that are affected by the explosion in prices. One of the main consequences of giving agriculture support is that owners of marginal land are induced to bring it into cultivation. Wheat, as we saw, is being grown in Yorkshire adjacent to the very moors themselves; many tens of thousands of acres of hill and mountain land now carry flocks of sheep because it is profitable to do so; and numerous other examples abound. It means that the present high level of support has jacked up the price of all land that it is possible to farm regardless of the cost of doing so. 46,000,000 acres must be brought into the calculation.

The startling fact is that poor quality hill and mountain land has risen in price proportionately more than the good land. The Country Landowners Association publishes regularly a Land Price Survey and, as the quality of land sold each month inevitably varies, the figures are weighted to make allowance for such variation. According to their Survey, published in March 1982, the average price of farm land with vacant possession in England rose from £833 an acre in December 1972 to £1,652 an acre in December 1981. But in Wales the increase has been from £391 to £1,235. When figures were published in the June 1981 issue of the CLA Journal, *The Country Landowner*, for the previous year, the opposite page was entirely given over to an advertisement which helped – inadvertently, of course – to explain that difference of 50 per cent. As anyone familiar with the Welsh countryside knows, much of the uplands have been blighted by bracken for many years past. The advertisement reads:

There are many reasons why now is a good time to go in for bracken clearance. It is known that landowners who have gone in for bracken clearance are now returning higher net incomes and thus better weathering the recession. Also, in addition to cash flow improvements, there are benefits through disease eradication, stock control and increased land value. With the increased subsidy to hill farmers and the Government grant for land improvement of up to 50 per cent of the approved cost of bracken control and follow up treatment – the cash is available.

Accompanying the advertisement is a photograph of the aircraft to be hired for spraying a particularly potent weedkiller. The land becomes more valuable; and more money flows into the coffers of the aircraft company. Looking at the agricultural Estimates for the Welsh Office, one gleans a little more about the money available. Under item D.1., 'Aids to assist favoured farming areas', £30,780,000 was allocated in the year 1980/81 alone and a further £14,000,000 for capital improvement. Incidentally, there are grants for the control of pests, including foxes, worth £4,000. A mere bagatelle and scarcely worth recording, but one wonders whether even a modest sum should be given to control foxes and rabbits; the greater the menace to a farmer, the greater the incentive to get together with his neighbours to deal with it, one might think.

How then do we assess the artificial price of 46,000,000 acres? There is, of course, no true average acre. In Holland, Lincolnshire, some of the richest land of all has been sold for £4,000 an acre – for farming, I hasten to add, not building. Before the war the price would have been about £250, so the owners of our best land have been almost denied excess value. Across in Montgomeryshire, I have seen land so hilly as to be unploughable valued at £1,000 an acre. And 30 years ago the owner would have been lucky to have got £15 an acre for it. So the present excess value is £725.

With the aid of the Ministry's grading of agricultural land

and by referring to the farm sales reported in the *Farmers'*
Weekly, we can build up a reasonably accurate estimate of the
excess value of farmland in the UK.

Table III

	Acres	1939 value per acre × 15	Actual value per acre	Excess value per acre
Grade I	1,263,628	£750	£3,000	£2,250
Grade II	6,588,921	£600	£2,500	£1,900
Grade III	22,068,374	£375	£1,500	£1,125
Grade IV	8,890,531	£150	£1,000	£ 850
Grade V	6,318,144	£ 75	£ 750	£ 675

The greatest increase in the value of land has been among
poorer grades, and as their owners have been the largest
beneficiaries of the grants and subsidies and all the other
inducements 'to go arable' it is not altogether surprising. Now if
we multiply the acreage of each grade of farmland by the excess
value as shown in the last column of the table, we see how our
land has been artificially inflated in value by the system of
support.

Grade I	£2,841,750,000
Grade II	£12,517,200,000
Grade III	£24,826,500,000
Grade IV	£7,556,500,000
Grade V	£4,264,650,000

Adding up these figures, we come to the astounding total of
£40,040,600,000. Thus it can be argued that the amount of
capital invested in farmland is £40 thousand millions more than
it would have been, but for the policy of agricultural support
pursued since the war. Put somewhat less charitably, those
fortunate enough to own farmland are richer by that amount.
And looking at it through the eyes of an economist who sees
British industry starved of the capital necessary to modernise
itself and adapt itself to the great technological achievements
that have been made, as so many of its competitors have done, it
means £40 thousand millions have been diverted away from

efficiency to inefficiency. What a diversion of capital! The luckiest beneficiaries are the very few who have continued to own farmland – or marginal land that has become farmland – over the last 30 or 40 years. Having bought at £25 an acre in, say, 1945 they have been able to mortgage their land at £200 an acre in 1960 and redeem it in the depreciated pound notes of 1982, having borrowed at a fixed rate 6 per cent on which they have obtained tax relief each year.

At the other end of the scale of fortune may be the small farmer who has managed to earn a livelihood with less than 100 acres, now finding himself driven to making the highest bid at the auction of his neighbour's property. Another 100 acres will make him 'viable', so he is told, and he has to borrow £100,000 at 17 per cent.

Anyone associated with farming knows how readily bank managers have offered to lend their money on the security of a farmer's title deeds. The total amount lent to agriculture is now just over £4,000,000,000. No one would suggest that none of this money should have been lent; nonetheless, it is proper to ask whether agriculture has borrowed more than it would have done, had there not been the present high level of protection.

The answer lies in the mouths of the bankers themselves. In recent years, there is not a bank chairman, chief general manager, local director, or even branch manager on record saying anything bearish about agriculture. Better to lend against land than a shop, a factory, or indeed any other business enterprise, especially if it is a small or medium-sized one. The very large companies – the kind that give the banks so much business that they can insist on the lowest rate to borrow money, the so-called blue chip rate – have little difficulty in borrowing as much as they want. There may be a hundred of such companies. But what of the rest? The future wealth and prosperity of Britain is at least as dependent upon these in the aggregate as it is on the existing top one hundred.

Let us assume, for the purpose of the argument, that agriculture had borrowed one-quarter of what it has succeeded in getting from the banks today. That would mean that the bank managers of Britain would have funds to the extent of £3,000,000,000 available for all the other small and medium sized businesses. It represents very many thousands of pounds for each of them.

Yet a reduction to one-quarter may be an underestimate. In 1979 agriculture borrowed £1,982,000,000 from the banks. Ten years before it was only £546,000,000. In 1959, £259,000,000; in 1949, £127,000,000; and in 1939 a mere £63,000,000.* These figures must go a long way to confirm that the higher the degree of protection and support given to agriculture, the greater the prospect of it being able to borrow the capital it wants. This is another and a serious example of the way capital has been diverted from the efficient to the inefficient.

Two further comments may be added. The first is that, on the principle 'to him that has, it shall be given', the large farmers have received the lion's share of this fresh capital. The banks realise that the small farmer is forever being squeezed out: as the number of holdings of fewer than one hundred acres grows less each year, so does the risk of lending to the small farmer increase. It does not mean that the small farmer is necessarily less efficient, but it is certain that the system of state interference since the war has added artificial problems for the small man which would not have arisen for him if the state had not interfered. While it may be understandable for the banks to prefer the large farmer to the small one, it makes it more difficult for the latter to compete.

The other comment is that this huge sum of borrowed money does not include loans to the industries that service agriculture. Shell, BP, ICI, Ranks Hovis McDougall, the Imperial Group, Boots, and British Leyland are among the large companies that have undoubtedly reached their present size because they have shared in the advantages of agricultural protection. Their borrowings from the banks compare with the amounts that have gone direct to agriculture. The total amount of capital invested in these companies that are supplying and servicing agriculture runs into thousands of millions of pounds; and, of course, only a part of it would be needed if Britain pursued a different agricultural policy.

* Financial Statistics, May 1981; Bank of England Statistical Abstract: 'Financial Statistics – UK Banks 1880-1962': D.K. Sheppard.

It is not possible to assess precisely how much extra capital has been absorbed by these companies, but it cannot possibly be less than £1,000,000,000. To those who may question that figure, it may be said that the capital employed in the industries that supply fertilisers, compound feeds and agricultural machinery is many times more than that. They are only three, albeit probably the three largest, industries that have expanded along with agriculture.

Industries that supply or service agriculture are themselves a source of capital for farmers. The competition between compound feed companies is so great that it has been quite normal for them to provide most of the initial capital for someone beginning a pig or poultry enterprise, and they may allow him credit up to a year. Machinery distributors may reach a similar agreement with a newcomer to arable farming. The total amount lent in this way, while important to agriculture, may be only a small fraction of creditors' resources. As the loans would come from the capital employed by the company, and therefore be part of the above estimate of £1,000,000,000, they must not be added as a separate item of capital diverted.

Loans advanced by the Agricultural Mortgage Corporation should undoubtedly be included in the calculations. The AMC is a quasi-official body that exists to provide working capital to the farmer who is an owner-occupier. On March 31st 1947 they had loans outstanding of £8,205,842; but on March 31st 1982 the outstanding loans were £412,915,437. I think we all have to agree that if farmland had risen in price at the same rate as inflation, these loans would have been considerably less. Taking into account the excess value of land as assessed above, it would be right to estimate the excess value of capital lent by the AMC as somewhere in the realm of £275,000,000, and such a sum is a further diversion of capital from other industries.

The insurance companies are another source of fresh capital. Like the banks they have been only too pleased to pour their money into agriculture in recent years. The same applies: every extra pound invested by the insurance companies in agriculture, because it is protected and supported, is a pound diverted away from other trades and industries which would otherwise have received that injection of capital.

35

The British Insurance Association submitted a memorandum to the Northfield Committee in which it set out the extent to which the insurance companies have invested in land. In 1966 they owned 83,090 agricultural acres. By 1977 they had increased it to 270,000 acres. That in itself is a useful commentary how this branch of the City has changed its mind about the potential return to be obtained from agriculture.

The memorandum did not reveal the amount of capital that had been diverted in this way, but it did the following breakdown in the type of farming:

Predominantly arable:	132,757 acres
Predominantly dairy:	10,133 acres
Predominantly livestock:	21,880 acres
Predominantly mixed:	88,212 acres
Hill farms:	17,022 acres
Total:	270,004 acres

From this it can be seen that as would be expected they have chosen to buy the better quality land. Disregarding the hill farms, it is unlikely their holdings can be worth less than £1,000 an acre. This gives us a round figure of £250,000,000.

The memorandum also gives for each year the number of acres purchased by the insurance companies. They are:

1967	1,981 acres
1968	50,805 acres
1969	10,160 acres
1970	7,992 acres
1971	7,152 acres
1972	10,876 acres
1973	21,231 acres
1974	31,437 acres
1975	24,112 acres
1976	21,424 acres
1977	24,744 acres

It is plain that their interest in agriculture burgeoned forth once we entered the EEC, and the years 1973 to 1977 also saw the steepest rise in the price of farm land. We can infer from this that the £250 millions of insurance funds diverted into agriculture is probably a significant underestimate. Further, the BIA accounts for 95 per cent of the insurance industry and funds invested by the remaining 5 per cent are excluded, but let us keep to our round figure. It is another item of capital that would have been invested elsewhere.

British agriculture has become not just capital intensive, but the most capital intensive of all our industries. This is the judgment – or is it the confession? – of the Country Landowners Association. In January 1978 they submitted a memorandum to the Treasury in which they disclosed that for every person employed in agriculture there was an investment capital of £38,000. This, they said, compares with £16,000 for the chemical industry, which the less well informed may have assumed to be the most capital intensive of all. The memorandum went on to say that the annual investment in agriculture equals £804 per person employed in the industry and that it is 30 per cent higher than in industry as a whole. The CLA has given the game away.

What then is the grand total amount of capital that has gone to agriculture as a result of a policy of protecting and shielding it from overseas competition, and has therefore been taken away from others who would have made more efficient use of it? This sort of reckoning is always difficult, and some readers may think that simply adding together all the figures I have listed would involve an element of double accounting (though others may find omissions). Nevertheless, by any reckoning the grand total must come to many thousands of millions of pounds. If the reader divides whatever total it may be by the British population (a mere 55,000,000) one is still left with a fortune – and a large one to the ordinary man in the street. But divide the total by the number of British who are in their work creating wealth, as distinct from consuming it, as most of us are, and then one realises what a burden is this policy of protection and subsidy on the back of the British people.

A misuse of resources sounds an innocuous term – a piece of economic jargon that may mean very little. The reality is that any misuse of the country's resources, be it capital, land, labour or its natural resources, is an act of impoverishment. The more the resources of Britain are misused, the more the people of Britain are pushed towards a lower standard of living and are deprived of what they could otherwise have.

3/The Diversion of Land and Labour

It has frequently been said, ever since the war, that every year agriculture loses some 50,000 acres of land. The Parliamentary Secretary to the Ministry of Agriculture, answering a Parliamentary Question, said: 'The average yearly loss of agricultural land to development or other uses, excluding woodlands, in England in the five-year period ending June 1980, was 18,500 hectares or 45,800 acres.' (Hansard, 16 April 1981.) If the process goes on we will, in the next century, lose all our good quality land. Moreover, as most of this development is near our existing towns or in other areas which have been regularly farmed for many years, the problem is worse than the bare statistic suggests. Nearly all of it is on agricultural land of Grades I, II, and III, and virtually none on Grades IV and V.

There is a slight fallacy in the way this statistic is used to illustrate the loss of food-producing land, as not all our home-grown food is produced by agriculture. For sheer productivity, it is difficult to beat the suburban vegetable garden, where each square foot may provide two crops every year. It is possible with a density of, say, six houses to the acre for those six gardens to produce more actual food than that same acre did when it was being farmed.

That, however, is incidental to the main comment that needs to be made about this great annual loss of agricultural land. It is that cultivated farmland is not, on the published figures, being lost to any serious extent. The Annual Review of Agriculture, which is presented to Parliament by the Ministry of Agriculture, sets out the 'total tillage' for each year. It is the total number of acres given over to arable crops, temporary grasses being excluded, but wheat, rye, barley, oats, mixed corn, potatoes and sugar beet all coming within the total. These Annual Reviews, deriving their facts from the Ministry's census

38

every year, confirm that cultivated farmland is not decreasing in area.

In 1953, total tillage was 12,304,000 acres. After fourteen years, when some 700,000 acres of our farmland must have been swallowed up in development, there were 12,354,000 acres of total tillage, an increase of 50,000 acres, part of agriculture's triumph. Another ten years on, far from there being a loss of 500,000 valuable acres, 1977 sees 12,036,000 in total tillage: a fall of a mere 268,000 acres over twenty-four years. Since then the position has been reversed. In 1978, total tillage is 12,209,000 acres; in 1979, a further increase to 12,315,000 (more than in 1953), and the provisional figure for 1980 is given as 12,438,000.

How can we reconcile such stability, such consistent figures, with the assertion that 50,000 acres of land are lost by agriculture every year – a loss of 1,500,000 acres over thirty years? Perhaps the estimate is an exaggeration, yet we can see with our own eyes every day of the week housing estates, roads, factories that have been built in the last ten years. Every town and most villages have expanded in that time. Very many thousands of houses have been built and hundreds of factories; and almost always they have taken over farmland. As a general rule the nearer land is to the town, especially in the southern half of England, where most of this new development has taken place, the better its quality, because it has probably been cultivated for a longer time.

As so many thousands of acres have undoubtedly been transferred from agriculture, there seems to be only one way to explain the contradiction. Land that was previously permanent pasture, i.e. suitable for good grazing only, has been promoted to arable land, and land hitherto rough grazing promoted to permanent pasture. Indeed, previous rough grazing is now deemed arable land. I have mentioned wheat being grown on high ground adjacent to the Yorkshire moors. I have also walked across a huge field of some 150 acres on the North Hampshire Downs where the surface was covered less by soil than by flints – some the size of a football – yet again winter wheat was being grown there. Both those places would have carried some grazing sheep ten or fifteen years ago and anyone seeing those acres ploughed up would have considered the farmer out of his mind. Up to a point this new arable land has been improved by very heavy applications of fertilisers. The cost involved has been considerable, and a large part of it has been paid for by the taxpayer by way of fertiliser grants. Without those grants it is unlikely the farmers concerned would have embarked upon the task of trying to make such land suitable for arable crops.

Again, the Annual Reviews confirm statistically what the countryman can see every day. Twenty years ago, in 1961, land classified for 'rough grazing', and so quite unsuitable for an arable crop, came to 18,121,000 acres. Over the years these have been steadily promoted to cultivation; by 1972, over two million acres had ceased to be rough grazing; and by 1980 more than another four million acres. The precise figures deserve to be quoted because they highlight something of great significance: the amount of land in total tillage has become virtually the same as the area of rough grazing. Rough grazing is 12,547,000 acres and total tillage 12,438,000. We can contrast this with twenty years ago when it was, respectively, 18,121,000 acres and 11,049,000.

Seven million acres! Rough, old land; at an auction an acre might have gone for the price of a cow, and it could have been rented for next to nothing. Ill-drained and so wet that cattle might only be turned out on it in high summer, pretty useless for hay, requiring tons of lime and probably only fit for a few sheep – such was a typical acre of that rough grazing. In twenty years, those seven million acres of poor land have been transformed into agriculture's tillage: wheat, barley, sugar beet and other crops that can only prosper on improved soil. It is agriculture's triumph. It has made seven million acres – an area the size of Yorkshire, Lancashire, Durham and Northumberland combined – very valuable. But it has been done at a price; and the price has been shameful, and far in excess of the direct cost of improving those many acres, hundreds of millions of pounds though that has been.

This diversion of land use has been paid for by the public in three ways. The taxpayer has provided most of the money for the actual improvement. The consumer has paid a higher price

40

for the food it yields; in the case of wheat, for example, it has been double the price, for this old rough grazing, despite being 'improved', remains in the same climate and generally speaking the cost of producing wheat on it is at least twice as much as in North America.

The third price is no less shameful, and it cannot be calculated in terms of pounds and pence. For generations, much of the land that has been classified as rough grazing has been free of barbed wire fences and other obstacles for those who might walk or ride over it. The Downs of Sussex, Hampshire, Dorset, Berkshire and Wiltshire are areas which include many thousands of acres which used to be open to the public, but which no longer are. Both rambler and rider would traverse miles in a straight line, doing no harm to anyone, and giving no one cause to complain. Exmoor has also been the scene of reclamation at public expense – and the public is now excluded from the acres reclaimed.

The NFU have admitted that in one year alone 700 acres of Exmoor have been converted into farmland. Derbyshire, Yorkshire and Lancashire have also witnessed similar diversions of land use. Is it important that a predominantly urban society should be able to stump across the hills and dales, or youngsters escape from the concrete that encircles their everyday life and find wide open spaces for the release of high spirits? Of course there are very many places still accessible for the visitor from city and town; but the number diminishes each year, and the fewer they become the harder it is for the owner to act as a tolerant host. A score of sports depend on an open countryside. If it is likely that a shorter working week will come about before the end of the century and the demand for such sporting activities continues to increase, a major problem will arise in meeting this demand. It is not a point to be overlooked if the British people want a higher standard of living.

Rather than divert this land into high-cost agriculture, a future generation might prefer us to leave it as it has been for countless years. This land cannot serve two masters: ought it not to serve the public in the way for which it is naturally best fitted?

Then there is the diversion of labour caused by a policy of

41

artificially enlarging agriculture. As with capital and land, any expansion of agriculture, if induced by government intervention, must cause more people to be employed in agriculture than would otherwise be the case; and employed less efficiently so far as the economy as a whole is concerned, just as both the extra capital and land used for an artificially expanded agriculture would be employed more efficiently if the government did not interfere.

British agriculture has had a remarkable record in productivity. Many a farm that once employed ten or fifteen men now has just one or two. This increase in productivity has outstripped anything achieved by any other country; and it cannot be matched by any other industry of any size in this country. Nonetheless, far too many pundits have accorded praise to British farmers for this achievement without detecting a flaw in the argument. Here is a typical example:

Farm incomes have been maintained only because of increased efficiency. This is a fact that must be heavily emphasised. One valid yardstick of efficiency is how much food can be produced on average by each individual who is engaged in the nation's farming. In the United Kingdom one man produces food enough for 23 people. In Denmark, it is 17; Federal Germany, 9; France, 8; and Italy, 7.

I wrote that myself in a booklet about agricultural policy in 1965.* Since then, productivity has improved still more. Now one man produces enough for 42 people. The other countries have also gone ahead, but they have remained behind us to the same extent as in 1965.

There is a fallacy in these figures that is very relevant in examining the way a heavily subsidised system of agriculture diverts manpower from efficient enterprises (those that can prosper without Government help) to those that are inefficient (those that cannot). The fallacy lies in the fact that there is not a single man left in British farming who produces an ounce of food without the aid of someone else, who is not deemed to be

---

* The purpose of the booklet was to argue the case for import levies instead of deficiency payments. It was severely criticised by the NFU at the time, yet it contained all the arguments that the NFU now employs to support an expansionist policy and, of course, they now favour import levies. I recognise that I am as inconsistent as they are in now contradicting myself in writing this book!

engaged in agriculture at all. The man in Coventry who works on the assembly line making a tractor is not, statistically speaking, engaged in agriculture, although he is as much in the process of food production as the man who drives it in the field. So too are the many thousands of men who are manufacturing or transporting the artificial fertilisers that have taken the place of the farmyard manure. While the number of people directly employed as farmers or farmworkers has fallen drastically in the years since the war when we have pursued a protectionist policy, the number indirectly employed by agriculture has increased just as drastically. Whole new industries have come into being with the sole object of supplying and servicing our farms. Had they not come into existence our countryside would not have been blighted by the social evil of rural depopulation.

There could well be as many as half a million men and women whose livelihood depends, in some degree, on the taxpayer continuing to subsidise agriculture. By taxpayers, I mean not just those who pay income tax, but everyone who eats, because every plate of food is affected by import duties and levies, which are just as much taxes as income tax or VAT. To assess accurately the precise number is difficult as it is necessary to disentangle a veritable cobweb of statistics. It is one of the features of protectionism that the good that is done to a few people is visible, while the harm done to the many is invisible.

The harm done to the many includes the three million who are unemployed. Although they are among the poorest they are deprived of the right to buy their food from sources considerably cheaper. Much more than that, how many of them would still have a job if a massive amount of capital had not been taken away from the industries that once were able to employ them, and given instead to the owners of the seven million acres?

4/The Diversion of Natural Resources

Government support of agriculture has caused two natural resources to be diverted to it on a massive scale: oil and fertiliser. In both cases the diversion has been artificial and would never have taken place to the extent it has but for the policy of support.

Sir Kenneth Blaxter of the Rowett Research Institute, in one of the most refreshing papers ever delivered to the Annual Oxford Farming Conference, in 1978, illustrated how oil has been swallowed up by British agriculture. Before we had tractors, he said, our farmers produced 41 per cent of the food we ate. Now, with the aid of tractors, they produce 46 per cent of our food. The population during those years has increased from 38 million to 56 million, so yield has doubled. But – here is the rub – it has needed a sixteen-fold increase in power consumption to achieve it. Moreover, he calculated that producing, processing and distributing our food used up 26 per cent of the nation's energy.

The nation's energy consumption is 209,300,000 tonnes of oil or oil equivalent; 26 per cent of that is 54,000,000 tonnes or rather more than one tonne to the acre. Obviously, it does not work out like that as the figure also includes fuel used up by the processors and distributors, but it is nonetheless quite a startling quantity. Until recent years, of course, this oil had to be imported and was an item in our balance of payments current account. The NFU and the oil companies who have campaigned so successfully for an expansion of British agriculture on the ground that it would 'save money' on the balance of payments would never concede that nearly all such 'saving' would be eliminated by a contrary entry for imported oil. Their argument is not validated by us now being, in effect, self-sufficient in oil: every extra pint of oil going to agriculture is another pint that cannot be exported.

The farmer is given every inducement to mechanise and buy ever larger and more powerful tractors and combine harvesters. He has the privilege – that word is used literally – of being able to set off the complete cost of any new machinery against income tax he is due to pay in the year of purchase. This is a most valuable tax concession; and the larger and more prosperous the farmer, the greater is its value to him.

No one can quarrel with cereals being grown in East Anglia because it is pre-eminently suitable for the purpose. But outside that area there are tens of thousands of farmers who have managed to make substantial profits out of wheat and barley since we entered the EEC; for wheat prices rose from under £30 a ton to over £100 once the import levies were introduced under the Common Agricultural Policy. Many of these farmers who ploughed up their pasture to take advantage of these high prices have had incomes of over £50,000 a year. By investing in new and more powerful tractors and combine harvesters they have been able, quite legitimately, to avoid much of the income tax they would otherwise have had to pay. However, they have also been using twice the amount of fuel that the older ones used to need.

The smaller farmer, while sharing the tax privilege in theory, finds that his income is too modest to enable him to gain a comparable advantage. Besides, having fewer acres, he does not need to use one of the new type of very large tractors. It is one of several reasons why the present system of support tilts the balance in favour of the larger farmer and against his smaller neighbour. As such, it must have also contributed to the fall in the number of small farmers which takes place every year.

In mechanising our farms we have replaced manpower with oil. The transfer has been made because it was profitable to do so, but the profitability has been contrived and artificial, the result of government support. If the price mechanism had been allowed to operate without that intervention by the government, it is arguable that a more efficient use of both manpower and oil would have ensued. A man with his hoe who grows his own food is among the world's most efficient producers of energy; and the farmer who uses his own muscle finds it cheap, reliable and wasteless. While a tractor will

45

obviously enable him to produce a great deal more than he would with his hand tools, the optimum of efficiency is not likely to be attained by the taxpayer's money being used to induce him to become more mechanised than he would without that money. And if the taxpayer's money does not have that effect, there seems little point in giving it to him.

Perhaps it may not matter very much if we do exhaust our oil resources sooner than we need because of their unnecessary diversion to agriculture. Other forms of energy may be devised in the next century; and tractors and combines will be replaced by machines which work off forms of energy that are yet unknown. But although the energy in the universe is, for our own purposes, limitless, other kinds may cost more to bring into use, and once we have found them, we must be ready to pay the extra price.

On the other hand, fertilisers (more strictly speaking, artificial fertilisers) are finite. Their reserves are exhaustible. What is more, the ones we are using now are in danger of becoming exhausted sooner than we may realise. The consequence to the Third World, where millions of acres more must be cultivated lest as many millions of the human race starve, is desperately serious. These acres need fertilisers, and we are depriving them of what they need. It may seem sensible to improve our own marginal land so that it can grow arable crops, but it can only be done by applying fertilisers much more heavily than would be the case if those same fertilisers were made available on the better quality land that could be brought into cultivation in the Third World. It is a perfect example of the misapplication of resources.

George Allen, the Professor of Agricultural Economics at Aberdeen University, in an article in *Lloyds Bank Review*, July 1975, wrote some gloomy comments on this subject. He argued that there must be doubts as to whether the developing countries would be able to have fertilisers to the value of £32.5 million by 1985, the quantity that the United States Department of Agriculture has calculated as their minimum needs. India, Pakistan, and Bangladesh have not been able to maintain even their existing levels of fertiliser imports or buy them at reasonable prices. He concludes with this judgment:

We could be pushing ourselves into a situation where large scale famine and malnutrition would be directly attributable to a deficiency in plant nutrient, which could have been avoided if strict commercial consideration had been allowed to have had a greater weight in the balance of factors determining governmental fertiliser policy.

Mr Roman Garcia, in a paper entitled 'Some Aspects on World Fertiliser Production, Consumption and Usage', given at the University of Iowa in 1975, estimated that the developing countries needed to import 65 per cent of their nitrogen fertilisers. The more fertilisers we use in Britain and other developed countries for the purpose of improving our poorer quality land, the more we force up the price in the world market.

World fertiliser prices have increased about five-fold since 1970, and although the explosion of the price of oil has been a factor in this, nonetheless farmers in the developed countries have been able to afford to pay for fertilisers at these new prices, and so manufacturers have charged accordingly. This is borne out by the figures. The Fertiliser Manufacturers Association, which has thirty-five member-companies, publishes each year *Fertiliser Statistics*. The issue for 1981 shows how the consumption of nitrogen fertilisers in the United Kingdom has steadily increased from 979,900 tonnes in 1974/75 to 1,335,000 tonnes in 1980/81. The average annual increase for consumption has been 5.3 per cent over the last six years.

One of the reasons why our farmers have continued to buy the fertilisers is that for many years they were cushioned from the true world price by a government subsidy. Such subsidies have not been available for farmers in the developing countries and so they have had to reduce their purchases. There really cannot be any doubt that food production has declined in some of these countries and more people have gone hungry, even starved, as a result. In using the taxpayer's money to divert fertilisers away from developing countries, it may be said that there are moral as well as economic considerations. Is it morally right that it should be done?

Some major international companies have been responsible for this policy; ICI, British Petroleum and Shell are among

47

them. Their stake in a policy of agricultural support is enormous; and they and the others in the fertiliser business have been considerable beneficiaries. Not for nothing do they spend their millions upon advertising for even larger sales to farmers.

We know there are hundreds of millions of our fellow humans in the Third World who have too little to eat. How many of them would have a fair share of the world's supply of fertilisers if this policy were not pursued, we are not to know. But we can be sure that the greater the number who go hungry because of this policy, the greater the shame upon those who persist in arguing in favour of it.

Is There a Case
for Support?

5/Do We Need 'Security of Supply'?

It is only in the last few years that we have heard the argument about the need to secure our food supplies. No one would have dared raise it before we began to cut off the trading links with low-cost suppliers in the Commonwealth and elsewhere. Now we are told that it is sensible to pay an extra premium over world prices to be sure of getting the food that we want. Let us therefore not be 'pennyfoolish'; better to give the farmers a reasonable price for what they produce, although that price may be rather more than we might pay elsewhere, because in return we know they will not let us down.

It is a plausible argument, especially when it is accompanied by horrendous stories of a population explosion and a lengthening queue of human mouths to feed. We know also that in the middle 1970s there was a world wheat shortage and chaos in the world sugar market. Despite all that, the argument does not hold water. The elements of the argument are these:

(1) We have already witnessed shortages in the case of wheat and sugar that have made our supplies insecure;
(2) A hungry Third World will demand a fairer share of the existing food supply;
(3) We cannot rely upon other countries to give us preferences in the future;
(4) Our own farmers and those in the EEC can be trusted to give us that preference.

Let us look at each of those elements in turn to see whether any of them are valid.

It is perfectly true that the major suppliers of wheat reduced their production. They were the United States, Canada, Argentina and Australia; and there is no doubt that as a result a world shortage ensued. Each of the governments of those countries, by one means or another, induced their farmers to grow less wheat in the years immediately before 1974. The governments intervened because farmers, if left to themselves, would have continued to grow wheat as before, since for most of them it was their main livelihood. Why then should those governments feel it necessary to coerce their own citizens from producing what they wished? No one has dared suggest that their farmers were inefficient or their prices too high. On the contrary, it was because they were too efficient and their prices too low that their governments had to coerce them. Because their wheat was of the kind and quality that the world's markets wanted and because its low price could secure it a sale in the world market, the EEC with surpluses of wheat produced at high cost had to resort to a policy of dumping to get rid of what they did not want themselves. It has never placed any limit upon the quantity it has exported at subsidised prices. Whatever quantity it wanted to put on the world market, it did so; and however large the subsidy, the taxpayers of the Community paid the money. It has meant that however low the world price for wheat fell, it was forced to fall still further when the EEC sold. No low-cost producer, no matter how efficient, can compete against that kind of state trading.

The world food market has always, to some extent, been a place for dumping. No one can assess the size of a harvest when the ploughs first take to the field, not even when weeks later the seed is planted. Producers the world over are sufficiently conscious of the laws of supply and demand to know that it is rather foolish to begin the process of supplying a market if the demand is not to be there. The millions of food producers in 150 different countries must each make their estimate of what they can sell for a satisfactory return. Their main guide must be the price they received in the previous year, but that, of course, is seldom the same for any two years in succession.

The total supply of food will depend largely upon those millions of estimates, but whatever the food being produced, meat and dairy products as well as arable crops, the ultimate supply will be determined by the behaviour of the climate. A few days of extra sunshine in just one country can make a surprising difference; so also can another inch of rainfall.

The total supply of food will always be unpredictable. In a world where only a minority of the human race are rationed strictly and the majority are free to buy their food as they can afford it, the demand for food will also be unpredictable. A slight rise in the price of beef on a Thursday or Friday may cause a hundred thousand housewives in Britain to switch to pork or lamb for their weekend joint.

There can never be a nice tidy balance between supply and demand. The food trade nationally knows this, and internationally knows it even better. In those circumstances, it is not surprising that producers, when they have had a crop that exceeds their expectations, have been willing to dispose of some part of it at less than the cost of production. When done across the frontiers we may denounce it as dumping; and while it can cause difficulties to other producers, some degree of dumping is inevitable in conditions of a free market. However, no producer would want to sell at below the cost of production and he plans his production on the assumption that he will not do so. Thus, as a general rule, dumping, should it take place at all, is on a modest scale; and it is seldom that any serious or permanent harm is done to producers in other countries. That is the case in a free market, but when governments intervene by goading farmers into producing more than they would otherwise do, they are bound to increase the risk of dumping. And that is precisely what the EEC has done with numerous commodities.

In the case of wheat, the European Community has been a notorious dumper. Year after year, it has placed vast quantities on the world market and, as every ounce of it has been grown at high cost, its sale has only been possible with the aid of export subsidies. The EEC Commission, sensitive to the charge of dumping, does not make available – not even to our own Ministry of Agriculture – the cost of these subsidies. In its published Budget, the subsidies of all exported cereals are given in one aggregate figure. We can assume that most were for wheat. In 1980, £687 millions were spent in this way; in 1979, it was £744 millions; and in 1978 it was £517 millions.

Export subsidies paid out on this scale, and paid out year after year, have a most damaging effect on other exporters. Australia, for example, used to have a valuable market for her wheat in Sri Lanka; it was virtually destroyed by the EEC. The worst effect is that no bona fide exporter can anticipate the quantity of wheat that is to be dumped on the world market by the EEC. Unless he also is to be subsidised by his own government, he faces the dangers of both losing some part of his export market and finding he must sell his wheat at a loss. It is small wonder he loses confidence and decides to plant another crop or put some of his acres back to pasture.

A decision to reduce production will not be made by just a few isolated farmers. It never works like that. When confidence is lost, it is lost by many. Most of the best wheat producers of the world cut their production or were so disheartened that they went out of business altogether. But their land is still there, waiting to grow wheat again at low cost.

Sugar is the other commodity that is mentioned to support the 'security of supply' argument. We are reminded that in 1974 the world price rocketed to over £600 a ton and housewives had to queue for their rations. A kindly Common Market came to the aid of its new members and sold us sugar at less than half the world price.

I was giving a talk to the Mauritius Chamber of Agriculture when news came through that the world price had reached £200 a ton. Although the Mauritius economy depends upon sugar and some 80 per cent of its export earnings come from sugar, the news was greeted by a mixed reaction. All those present knew well enough that the world price for sugar is very volatile, and this is not surprising because it is an artificial creation. About 88 per cent of the sugar that is exported was sold then under the International Sugar Agreement or the Commonwealth Sugar Agreement; their purpose was to provide stability of prices for sugar growers, most of whom are in developing and poor countries and are for various reasons unable to grow other crops. Hence only some 12 per cent of the sugar exported had its price fixed by day-to-day free market forces. Most of this sugar went to Canada and Japan, and a few smaller countries where consumption was low. The smaller the quantity in a free market, the more uncertain and volatile is the price likely to be. The Mauritius growers realised that an excessively high price in one year would prompt an over-optimistic expansion of

54

production for the following year, and the consequent glut would cause havoc in the limited free world market.

This is what happened in 1968. The world price fell as low as £13 a ton for a short while and was about £20 a ton for much of the year. The latter price represented roughly half the cost of production. Not every sugar producer was affected, especially the smaller producers who sold all their crops under the Commonwealth Sugar Agreement, so the collapse of the world market was not the catastrophe one might have expected. But the essential reason why the world market collapsed was because of a coincidence of, firstly, an unusual growing season and, secondly, the dumping by the EEC of one million tons of sugar onto this narrow world market. Canada and Japan bought what they wanted from Europe at bargain prices.

The experience of 1968 was not forgotten. In our negotiations to enter the EEC in 1970-72 it was uppermost in the minds of the Commonwealth producers. They knew the principle of Community preference, that once we were inside the Common Market we would have to conform to a policy that required us to buy our sugar from within the Common Market in preference to any that was available outside, regardless of whether the latter was naturally cheaper. I visited several of the producing countries at the time to explain the dangers of the CAP to the leaders of the sugar industry. For them, the most important was the end of the Commonwealth Sugar Agreement. The best that Mr Heath was able or willing to do for them was to get Brussels to 'take to heart' the needs of the Commonwealth producers in the developing countries, i.e. all of them except Australia.

This assurance was futile as the basis for confidence; and it is to the credit of the Labour Government that in renegotiating our terms of entry they secured permanent access for 1.3 million tons of sugar a year from the developing countries of the Commonwealth.

But the new agreement was not finally established until 1975; and indeed it might never have been obtained at all if the shortage of 1974 had not occurred. And, of course, it was before 1974 that Mr Heath had struck the blow to their confidence. By then the Commonwealth Sugar Agreement was dissolved, the sugar producers were apprehensive for their future and

55

convinced that Britain was deceiving them. They could not forget their history. Maybe it was long ago, but every occupant of the Carribean islands, Mauritius and Guyana knows that his country was peopled to grow sugar for us, and that their forefathers were torn from their homeland and transported to a different continent, enslaved and humiliated in the process, to satisfy the sweet tooth of the Englishman.

Then came the sugar shortage in the world – almost the first there has ever been and one never likely to be repeated. The sugar crop failed in two key countries, and the free world market went into disarray. If the Commonwealth Agreement had continued – as it would have done if we had not joined the EEC – our own supplies would have been secure, for the Commonwealth producers had enough for our needs. But why should they give Britain preference when they had a chance of gaining a place in the world market and opening up for themselves an outlet for their produce to replace the one they had lost in Britain? It was obvious that they had to act as they did.

Cynics have asserted that they would have done the same anyway, whether or not we had joined the EEC, but it would have been particularly stupid of them to break the terms of the Commonwealth Sugar Agreement, especially at the very time that the Agreement would have been renewed. The Agreement survived nearly a quarter of a century; in those years the Commonwealth acted honourably although there were occasions when producers could have made a short-term gain by acting dishonourably. The Agreement gave Britain secure supplies of sugar and it gave the producer a secure market. Although the so-called world price was sometimes above and sometimes below the price in the Agreement, both parties were given stability.

As with wheat the example of sugar does not prove that an extensive policy of supporting agriculture is necessary to secure supplies. Indeed, the contrary is the case. Only a few years ago our sugar beet crop was disastrous. It was blighted by a yellow leaf disease and the disease could have affected every acre of sugar beet in the Common Market. Another year like that and we could have witnessed the spectacle of Europeans scrambling in the world market as the price rocketed upwards.

The second element in the argument about secure supplies is that a hungry Third World will demand fairer shares of the existing world supplies. This really turns on the word 'demand', which has two meanings. There is the everyday one, in the sense that we ask for something in a firm and determined way; and there is the economists' meaning. By muddling up the two, this part of the argument gets muddled too.

A hungry Third World may need more food, but demand, in the economists' sense of the word, implies both need and a capacity to buy. Now if the Third World can demand in this sense the supply will be forthcoming. World food production could be doubled without any practicable difficulty (I will come back to this again in a later chapter) and it is not necessary for anyone to go hungry, let alone starve or suffer from malnutrition. The earth is there, the skills are there, the seed, the stock and all the tools and machinery could be made available within a few years.

Is there any risk of the other kind of demand? We are given the example of oil and how the members of OPEC have ganged up against the rest of the world. Could the suppliers of certain kinds of food do the same? The answer must be a resounding 'no'. We can list the food stuffs that could possibly be controlled by a Third World cartel. They are cocoa, coffee, tea, rice, sugar and bananas. But what else? I doubt if any other items can be added to that short list, other than some exotic fruit which we could well do without. This brings home to us an essential fact about Third World agriculture that I will return to later: it is that economic colonialism has, by fair means or foul, expropriated the greater part of the most productive land in the Third World, so that it yields crops mainly to be exported to the developed countries.

There was a time when these developing countries grew a variety of crops to provide for their own needs and those alone. Of course, there were famines that accompanied droughts and there were other disasters that caused many to go hungry or starve (as they do today), but the evidence is clear that many of them carried larger populations than they do today, especially those in Africa; and their system of agriculture, although primitive, was able to produce a sufficient range of goods to enable each country to be broadly self-sufficient.

Economic colonialism changed all that. Monoculture was introduced. If one country was better fitted to grow cocoa than bananas then the Western planters so arranged it. Thus Ghana concentrated upon cocoa, Ceylon on tea, Brazil on coffee, Jamaica on sugar, and so on. The decisions were not taken by the farmers themselves, but by European or American-based companies that were established to set up the plantations. Control still vests, for the most part, with such companies. Are they likely to promote a cartel to deprive their fellow-Europeans or fellow-Americans of any of these foods?

One attempt has been made to emulate OPEC. In 1974, the five countries producing most of the bananas decided to set up OBEC (the Union of Banana Exporting Countries). Their governments decided to impose on every box of bananas an export tax that varied from some 12 pence to 30 pence. The attempt has been an almost total failure. The great corporations, such as United Brands, that effectively control the world market, refused to pay the tax, threatened to abandon the plantations they owned, or resorted to bribery to reduce the tax, so that the cartel to all intents and purposes soon came to an end. Three of the international banana corporations (United Brands, Castle and Cook, and Del Monte) used the export tax, even when it was not paid, as an excuse to reduce their purchases, and at the same time increased their prices to the customers so that their profits on each box of bananas increased from 10 pence to about 30 pence.

The banana countries having failed, it is unrealistic to expect those countries producing coffee, tea or any of the other foodstuffs to succeed. Competition between them is equally intense, nor can the governments themselves successfully impose a cartel without the cooperation of the plantation owners. Moreover, they know that the risk of failure is made the greater because they are trading, not in foods that are essential to the needs of the West, but in luxuries to which there is always an alternative.

Now let us look at the third element in the argument – that we cannot rely upon other countries to give us preferences in the future. Just for a minute let us imagine that some disaster overtook Britain that made it impossible to grow any food at all, or that Britain decided that as from a certain date, say three or four years from now, no food at all would be produced on our island. No milk, no potatoes, no meat, no vegetables, no eggs, no butter or cheese, no fruit of any kind. At the same time it is also announced that our ports would be opened to any ship bringing in food and that all tariffs, levies, quotas and all the other restrictions on the import of food were to be abolished. Would we go hungry?

We can imagine how the news would be received among the farmers and food manufacturers of the world. It would be a veritable sensation. In all those countries like Argentina, Australia, New Zealand, South Africa, Brazil and Canada the exporters would look across to us, as they used to do, and once again study our market. They would conclude that Britain is the most perfect market for the export of food. It has everything they want. In the first place, its people are among the most prosperous in the world. Everyone has a guaranteed income; even the unemployed, the sick and disabled receive enough money from the state to enable them to buy a reasonable amount of food. Every one of its 55 million people would be purchasers; they would want food and they would be able to pay for it. They are very different from the 400 million in other countries who want food but go hungry because they have no money to pay for it. That fact removes the first anxiety of the prospective exporter of food to us. Next he looks at the British market and finds that nine-tenths of the consumers live in or near large towns, that communication to them all from the ports is cheap, speedy, and efficient. Again, how different from other countries where the cost of distributing food to the consumer adds a disproportionate amount to the cost of the food itself. Then the food exporters in all those countries would see who would be doing the importing in Britain, and they would rub their hands with glee! More than half the food sold in Britain goes through supermarkets which have central buying agencies. A few days spent in London, in the offices of Tesco's and Sainsbury's, and the contract is signed. Now that is not how they sell to other countries where the retail markets may be in the hands of thousands of independent shopkeepers who may not be tied to any one importer or distributing middle-man.

All these are major tangible advantages to the exporters, but the greatest, most helpful and most positive advantage of all would be the knowledge that access to the market was assured. Whoever could supply the needs of the British people at the lowest cost would get the orders – that would be the signal that went out to them. The exporters of Argentina, Australia and the others could then accordingly go to the farmers and say to them 'We have a market which is secure.' It would be the only market in the world – with the exception of Hong Kong – that was truly open, where no government would intervene arbitrarily and, without warning, exclude imports of food. In a word there would be total security. Security of supply is important to the consumer, but security of demand is vital to the producers. No one is going to produce food unless he is reasonably certain that it will be sold at the price that he can afford to sell it at. Where is the farmer who is willing to buy or rent land, purchase or hire his ploughs and tractors, then cultivate his land, sow his seed and nourish his crop and, months later, bring in his harvest, unless he has some security in his mind that his years of labour and his working capital will have their reward?

If Britain were to say to the food producers of the world 'Our ports are open: provided you can grow your food more cheaply than our farmers, you will be assured of a market in Britain,' we can be sure that they would reciprocate, rather than lose such a market. It would be their sheer self-interest to do so. Then Britain could be sure that her people would have preference over all others. Greater security of supply is impossible to conceive.

Finally, there is the fourth element in the argument, namely that our own farmers and those in the EEC can be trusted to give us preference over other outlets. This is undoubtedly true if food prices are higher within the EEC than outside. As that is normally the case, and is certainly likely to remain the position in the future, it is obvious that our farmers must dispose of their produce on the home market. They have no other choice. But if a market outside the EEC offers them a higher price we cannot be sure that their charitable sentiment will outweigh their own interest. While it is true that export controls can always be introduced to make sure that their food stays here, the real weakness of this element of the argument is that it fails to recognise that farmers themselves do not make the ultimate decision as to how much food is grown. At least once in a generation both Britain and Western Europe suffer from a prolonged drought that may reduce cereal yields by 20 per cent or more. A few years ago, as noted already, sugar beet was affected by a disease that made much of the crop quite useless. The scourge of foot-and-mouth could devastate our home supplies of beef and lamb. These are the occasions when we are forced to turn to the world market; and the narrower it becomes, with other countries pursuing a policy of self-sufficiency, the higher the price we must pay for such imports.

Agriculture is, in fact, 'unplannable'. No group of high powered officials can ordain how much food will be grown at home, no matter how large the battery of computers to assist them, nor how skilful they may be in marshalling their research, nor even how great their authority may be in ordering farmers what to do. Whatever their forecast, it will always be more than what is ideally desired, or less.

It might be just possible to base an autarchic, mercantilist policy upon a calculation of how many gas ovens, refrigerators and deep freezes will be made and sold in any one year. To make a further calculation about the quantities of all the different kinds of food that will be put inside them is far beyond the realm of any such possibility. The uncertainties for the consumer can only be minimised when he has access to supplies from every corner of the world.

6/A Starving World

There is no doubt that many millions of the human race do not have enough to eat and a tragically large number die from malnutrition. It is unfortunate that certain pressure groups, financed by international food companies, have persuaded so many of us that this evil can only be overcome by the richer countries becoming self-sufficient. The argument is plausible enough, yet it is the very opposite of the truth.

The human race is not like one large family eating its meal together, where if one eats more than his fair share, others must have less. Were that the case the argument would be incontrovertible.

The real scarcity is not of food but of people capable of buying the food that is available and could be made available. In a word, it is poverty that is the cause of hunger. This point has been made over and over again by the United Nations' Food and Agriculture Organisation, especially by Dr Boerma, its former Director-General. Much of this poverty is the direct result of the selfish policies of the developed countries in that, despite all the pretence to the contrary, the Lomé Convention included, a vast number of trade barriers exist to prevent the Third World exporting freely to us. At the same time the rampant inflation in the West has quadrupled or quintupled the price of our exports to them, many of them being essential for any improvement in their standard of living.

Let one example illustrate the effect of our inflation. In 1972 a Jamaican could grown 21 tons of sugar or 25 tons of bananas and he could sell them for the price of a new 78 hp tractor imported from England. In 1982 he would have to work twice as hard to grow 50 tons of sugar to buy the same kind of tractor, and it would be necessary for him to beaver away three times as hard as in 1972 to grown 76 tons of bananas for the tractor. Not only the Jamaican, but almost every food producer in the developing countries – and they produce little else but food – has been caught in a scissor movement: on one side, they have to pay even higher prices for what they buy from us; on the other, when allowance is made for inflation, reduced prices for what they are allowed to sell to us. The gap will continue to widen so long as the West continues its inflationary course, while at the same time it places numerous obstacles in the way of exports from the Third World. If we choose to make them poorer, we cannot be surprised to hear that they have less money to buy the food that they and their families should eat.

Both the FAO and the United Nations' other agency, the World Health Organisation, have published what they consider to be the nutritional requirements of the human race. Our age, sex, height, occupation and the climate we enjoy are obvious factors that vary our needs, and these have all been assessed in the tables they have prepared. They have also invented 'reference man'. He is aged 25, weighs 65 kilograms and spends eight hours in bed, eight at work and eight in non-occupational activities. While the amount of energy he exerts will depend on numerous factors, assuming his work and leisure engage him in moderate activity and the climate he lives in is neither excessively hot nor cold, such a man should have 3,000 calories a day. The world produces food at that rate for every man, woman and child in grain alone, that is wheat, rice, maize, barley and oats. One pound of grain provides not less than 1,500 calories and in 1977 the world's grain harvest amounted to 1,446,000,000 tonnes. Thus an equal distribution of these basic foods would, if it were practical, ensure that the world's population of 4,000 millions would all have enough to eat. It must be admitted that most of us in the developed countries would recoil from such a dreary diet, but it takes no account of any of the other kinds of food that would also be available if we were all given equal rations, especially the enormous quantities of fish, fruits and vegetables that could also be produced. An equal distribution of all food stuffs now available would provide nutrition in excess of what we need.

It will be noticed that I have not referred to eggs, meat, milk, butter and cheese. Modern methods of producing these require the use of concentrated feeds for the livestock that produce them. No less than one third of the world's grain goes into the mouths not of humans but of livestock to feed the relatively rich. Since the war it has become profitable for farmers not only in the United Kingdom but throughout Europe and the United States to feed intensively kept farm animals on grain rather than the kinds of feed they were given for centuries, and to keep them in expensive buildings instead of yards and fields. Farmers have not, of course, had to pay the true cost of putting their stock into this modern factory-style environment. Grants and tax allowances have been so munificent that only a part of the real expense has been theirs. Without this aid from the taxpayer it is doubtful whether these new methods of husbandry would ever have become so general, but as it is, farmers wishing to continue with extensive forms of farming find it hopelessly uneconomic trying to compete against those who take advantage of taxpayers' money. The example of free range eggs against the massive 10,000 bird batteries is the most obvious one. There is also the dairy farmer who believes it is healthier for his herd to remain out of doors and, for the several diseases to which they are prone, to be given plenty of space apart from one another – twenty cows on sixty acres was typical of dairy holdings twenty years ago. He cannot earn a livelihood now when a seventy-five cow herd is the norm, kept indoors for most of the time and fed a concentrated ration. Gone too, is the day a mixed farm could profitably keep a dozen sows, all put out to graze and improving rough pastures. It has no chance against the specialist with some two hundred sows kept permanently in stalls, not even able to turn round, and released only to farrow twice a year.

In the last decade the process of fattening beef out of doors on grass supplemented by hay and roots has given way to intensive methods in buildings costing many thousands of pounds to erect and each one the subject of a substantial grant of taxpayers' money. Notwithstanding the higher cost of grain-based feeds these forms of husbandry can succeed financially when the traditional ones will fail. Even the most efficient farmer usually works on a modest margin of profit, given the amount of capital he requires, so that all farmers, to survive, must emulate the methods of the most profitable. This may seem desirable, but it should also be remembered that this standard of profitability is phoney: it exists only because other people's capital from other parts of the nation's economy has been diverted to agriculture by means of taxation. If the government remained neutral in this respect, the profitability of such farming methods would evaporate. Among the beneficiaries would be many of the millions who now go hungry and whose suffering is a disgrace to humanity.

The lobbyists and log-rollers in Washington, London and Brussels who have done so much to persuade governments to support this policy insist that these intensive methods are essential and indeed should be extended to the Third World to meet the needs of a still greater population by the end of this century. Some 6,000 million human mouths will then exist, they say, an increase of 50 per cent.

The truth is that even if our numbers were to double no problem need arise because, as matters now stand, less than one half of the world's arable land is cultivated. The potential for increasing food production is nothing short of enormous. Several studies have been made on this vital – literally vital – topic. Perhaps the most important of them was *The World Food Problem: A Report of the President's Science Advisory Committee* published in 1967 by the US Government Printing Office. It showed that only about 44 per cent of the land potentially capable of growing arable crops was being cultivated; and all the evidence shows that despite more than a decade having passed, the percentage is still approximately the same.

At the World Food Conference in 1974, held under the auspices of the FAO, Monsieur Ibrahim, the Sudanese Minister of Agriculture, stated that only one-tenth of his country's arable land was being farmed; the proportion remains about the same today, despite the hunger of thousands living in Sudan. Throughout most of the African continent a similar story could be told. Nigeria and Tanzania are making determined attempts to raise their production of cereals and have a great deal of excellent land for the purpose. Zaire, however, has perhaps the greatest potential, with an incalculable acreage capable of producing food, yet a population with one of the worst dietary standards.

With 16 per cent of the world's land capable of being tilled, South America is the saddest example of how we are abusing our national resources. More than half of Colombia's good farmland stands uncultivated; in Ecuador it is 14 per cent; in Chile, Uruguay and Argentina, vast areas are idle. Brazil, it is said, could feed the entire human race. It is no exaggeration. It comprises more than 3,250,000 square miles, slightly smaller than the United States, but with soils capable of yielding crops much richer and larger. Of course, a considerable area of Brazil is yet to be explored, but enough is known to assess that her average arable yields would be not less than those in Britain. If this proved to be the case, those many square miles could, in years to come, produce enough wheat to provide one ton a year to everyone of the world's existing population. That is 6 lbs a day or 9,000 calories – three times more than 'reference man' needs to eat! No one who has visited Brazil would suggest that monoculture on so vast a scale is practical or desirable, and no sane person would want to destroy the Amazonian forests. But no one can leave Brazil unimpressed by what could be done to increase the world's food resources in a comparatively short period of time.

So long as the United States and the European Community dump surpluses of wheat onto the world market at prices that are artificially low, it is idle to expect that such resources as exist in South America and elsewhere will ever be properly used. A policy of genuine free trade, in which the rich and powerful among the nations stop subsidising their exports and penalising imports, would bring into cultivation these acres. There is no other way in which this can ever be achieved. The existing pangs of hunger among countless millions have failed to do so, that is sure.

Two further points can be made to rebut the argument that the plight of starving millions requires us to curb imports of food into Britain. The first is that different methods of husbandry could transform the world's consumption of food. One third of all the grain produced goes, as noted already, into meat, eggs and dairy products. Little is so used in China.

Chinese agricultural achievements in the last decade have verged upon the miraculous. Even its bitterest critics confess that few, if any, of its millions now go hungry. Yet this was a country that was once plagued by famines, by droughts that alternated with floods, and food crises that recurred with a terrible regularity. That everyone in China is fully employed is not unconnected with that achievement. High-cost and capital-intensive methods of farming are condemned as a matter of policy. Great schemes of reclaiming land, damming rivers, constructing canals for irrigation, are done by hand – tens of thousands of hands. The devastating floods, followed by equally destructive droughts, seem to be events of the past. The land itself is improved not by high-cost fertilisers but composts of vegetable waste and manure with even human excreta added, as our forebears used to do. Nor are expensive herbicides, pesticides and fungicides applied to poison the soil; it gets old-fashioned rotations and much hoeing instead. Most important of all, so far as the starving millions in the rest of the world are concerned, high-cost feeding compounds have no place in their system. While pigs in our own country are almost all now fed upon those compounds, in China they are fed on low-cost roots and waste human food. Their chickens, cows and other stock are fed on similar cheap principles.

It is true that China is still an importer of wheat; according to the International Wheat Council and other sources her imports have ranged from 3.5 million tons a year to 5.5 million. It has, however, been suggested that these are for a grain stock pile that has reached 40 million tons, a precaution against war or some national disaster.

The other point that the protagonists of extreme protection overlook is that the fertility of our land, and thus the quantities it will yield, is neither static nor permanent. Fertility will improve immeasurably by the right methods of use and cultivation. Most of Europe – say two centuries ago – used to consist of poor quality land; now it is much improved. The land in Japan was generally inferior to that of India; today the reverse is the case, and Japan's yields, having been less than India's, have now become five times greater. Good farming can indeed work miracles.

The conclusion seems irresistible. There is no reason to be filled with neo-Malthusian gloom about the world's population outpacing the capacity of the land to supply its needs. Experts are agreed that probably every country in the world, Hong Kong excepted, could, if it so willed, be self-sufficient; and that includes the United Kingdom. And some countries could feed many more than their own populations.

7/The Strategic Argument

After the 1939-45 war a favourite argument for supporting agriculture was the strategic need to grow a substantial proportion of our own food lest another war occurred. It was used to underpin the Agriculture Act of 1947 and it still lingers on although it tends to be mentioned rather hastily, even incidentally, as if it no longer stood up to scrutiny.

During the war the fifty million people on our island fortress ate very much better than either our enemies or those they subjugated in Europe. It should have been the opposite: continental Europe being almost self-sufficient before the war and France always an exporter, the problem of feeding those millions should have been much easier. The bravery of our Merchant Navy is one part of the answer: another is that we began the war with a massive merchant fleet that existed because of the trade we carried on with so many countries across the seas. Our policy of free trade gave us that fleet; without it the number of our ships would have been many fewer. As it was, a large number were sunk by enemy action; appalling though their loss was, Britain was able to survive their destruction, but only because she had begun the war with a fleet of merchant ships large enough for all the trade she carried out. In comparison, the merchant fleets of the European countries were puny things.

Whilst it is true that food supplies can be cut off by blackmailing producers as well as an enemy navy, it would be rather churlish to contemplate our particular suppliers as being prone to blackmail. It was the producers of Australia, New Zealand, Canada and the United States who were steadfastly loyal to us during both world wars, and it is they who would fill the main gap if we reverted to a liberal policy of importing food.

Those who insinuate that blackmail is a danger fail to see

that, even if successful, if would achieve little for the offenders. The blackmail, presumably, would take the form of demanding an inordinately high price for the continued export to us of the food we needed. Our succumbing to the threat would have the effect of putting into the hands of the blackmailers a larger quantity of our currency, all of which would remain in this country where it would have to be spent.

The strategic argument for protection really rests on the assumption that a future war will not be a sudden nuclear holocaust, but a conflict that might be extended over a year or more. It is argued that it is in those circumstances that a strong agriculture capable of providing most of our needs should be part of our plans for national defence.

Again it is useful to draw on our memory of what happened in 1939. In that year we produced only about a quarter of the food we ate, and only a small part of our cereals. Most of our farmland was under grass and, in the war years that followed, millions of acres of that pasture – the equivalent of several counties – were ploughed up for the first time for generations. The resulting yields were quite remarkable. Very little in the way of artifical fertiliser was applied and there was not much farmyard manure to go round; the quality of seeds was mediocre and the skills of the farmers and farmworkers, who were more accustomed to livestock than arable farming, were not as good as they are today. Nonetheless, those millions of acres produced some marvellous crops. The reason was that grass stores up fertility, and for all the years that land was under grass it was storing up in the soil a great bank of fertility.

Much of the land reverted to pasture immediately after the war, but in recent years the high prices that have been paid for cereals have caused it to return to the plough. The green bank of fertility has gone. Come another war, it would not be possible to repeat the great achievement of the war years. In fact, in the event of another war, much of the expansion of our agriculture could not be sustained, and over a wide area there would be a cut back in agricultural production. The reason for this is that, to a dangerous degree, our present level of production has been made possible by increasing inputs that are imported from abroad and cannot be obtained from our own natural resources.

In 1939 the cart horse was still the main source of power on many of our farms; now it is exclusively the tractor, and unlike earlier and lighter models, the modern tractor, like the modern combine, uses an inordinate amount of fuel. Imported fertilisers have doubled the stocking rate for many a dairy herd, and enabled herds of beef cattle and flocks of sheep to graze land which would otherwise be incapable of supporting such numbers. Modern feeding stuffs include protein additives of soya bean or fish meal, both of which come from across the sea. A major decision would have to be made if we were plunged into another war: would it be right to endanger our already diminished merchant fleet and put in peril the lives of our seamen to bring to this country the oil, fertilisers and protein, so that British farmers could go on producing the kind of food we do now, and in the way we do so, or should British farmers adapt their methods of production to the need to save British ships and British lives?

Our modern and efficient farmers – efficient in the sense the word is used about agriculture – are not equipped to carry on in a seige economy. Anyone doubting that should visit a large dairy farm where a herd of more than 100 cows may flourish on, perhaps, as many acres. Remove imports of oil, fertilisers and protein and the farm would be lucky to keep half that herd.

So the strategic argument is not a valid one. Indeed for those reasons it is really a counter-argument. It can be stood on its head and shown to be a reason why we should return to the conditions before the war which enabled us to eat so much better than our enemies.

8/The Balance of Payments Myth

Another reason advanced for giving support to agriculture is the balance of payments. Agriculture, we are told, could save Britain another £1,000 millions on the balance of payments; and we are further assured by the NFU and others that 'agriculture is Britain's biggest import saver'. The premise of the argument is that imports are 'bad' and exports 'good'. It is a fable that has blighted our economic thinking ever since the end of the war. Successive Governments have exhorted businessmen to export, have set up agencies to underwrite the losses, converted half the Diplomatic Service into supernumerary salesmen and even gone so far as to give loans to foreigners to buy our exports at derisory rates of interest. While exporters are given knighthoods, importers are made to feel distinctly inferior and perhaps a little lacking in patriotism when they are told by their bank managers that *their* borrowings must be reduced.

The other countries that themselves have an adverse balance of payments with us are the ones that used to supply us with food. New Zealand, Australia, the United States, Argentina, Canada are the most notable examples. Because of the deteriorating terms of trade, New Zealand and Australia, in particular, have put up serious obstacles to our exports to them. Many of our businessmen have found it so difficult to export to those two countries that they have given up the effort. New Zealand and Australian consumers have lost the ability to choose a British-made article, and the British industrialist has lost a market that was once freely accessible.

The converse is equally true. The British people no longer eat the beef, butter and cheese from Australia and cannot eat as much lamb, butter and cheese from New Zealand as formerly because the producers have lost, entirely in the case of Australia and partly in that of New Zealand, the outlet they used to be allowed to have in Britain.

The balance of payments has become something of a nation's virility symbol. If 'strong', it is doing well, its statesmen can travel the world with their heads high and their visits abroad are solicited. As they come down the steps from their jet, the television cameras whirl to transmit a portrait of self-importance. The Minister of Finance of a country with a trading surplus is indeed important. He becomes a lender of money; the country with a deficit is beholden to him.

The reason for this is that a balance of payments is in fact a balance of payments – the payments must balance. Strictly speaking, it is not possible for a country to have a balance that is either favourable or adverse. The balance of payments is made up of two accounts, the current and the capital. The current concerns the exports and imports, both visible and invisible. Into this account go all the payments for visible and tangible items that are imported or exported, such as cars, television sets and other manufactured goods, together with food; also the 'invisibles' which are payments for services such as banking, insurance, and shipping. The total value of visible and invisible exports, amounting to some £20,000 millions in a year, is never likely to equal precisely the total value of visible and invisible imports. It is matched by a counteracting surplus or deficit in the capital account. When Britain has a balance of payments deficit in the current account, she has a surplus in the capital account – and each sum is exactly the same because the two accounts must balance.

Pound notes are intrinsically useless pieces of paper. Their value exists as a means of exchange in Britain; once out of this country they can still, with difficulty sometimes, be exchanged, but they remain valueless until they return to Britain. Thus pound notes do not in practice leave these shores. If an exporter to Britain is paid in pound notes they stay here and are spent by him in this country. However, virtually all imports are paid for in the currency of the exporter's own country; and in the world of today the necessary currency is bought in the foreign exchange market.

It is this institution, hectic but fascinating, that makes trade multilateral and not bilateral as it used to be. It no longer matters (even if it ever did) for one country to have an adverse 'balance' with another. Great concern is expressed at the way we import more from Japan than she imports from us, and she is criticised for not taking steps to restrict her exports or to increase imports from us. She has been warned that failure to do so will invite retaliation. A moral obligation is invoked; Japan ought to buy more from us because we have increased our purchases from her, as if some code of international ethics existed which prevailed over the simple proposition that a willing seller and a willing buyer should be allowed to do business together.

People who think like that – and they are in high places – do not seem to understand how the foreign exchange market operates. The Japanese television set is sold for pound notes to a British customer. The retailer, wholesaler and the importer himself trade in pound notes as, of course, they must when the transaction takes place in this country. The Japanese exporter, however, needs to be paid in yen, so the British importer arranges with his bank the purchase of sufficient yen to pay for the imported television sets. The bank's representative buys the yen in the London foreign exchange market from a dealer who may have bought as a result of a transaction that has taken place thousands of miles away in a quite different currency. The currencies themselves have never any cause to leave their country of origin. Sterling, dollars, francs, yen, pesetas, marks and dozens of other currencies are being bought and sold every day in the foreign exchange market. The more a country trades with others, the more its currency is in demand. Obviously, if a country is exporting – visibly and invisibly – more than she is importing, the demand for her currency will exceed supply and this will cause its value to go up in the foreign exchange market. Whether the increase in value will be reflected in a higher rate of exchange must depend upon its freedom to float.

When a government fixes the rate of exchange of its currency it has to intervene in the market by borrowing in other currencies if it is a net importer or lending its own currency if a net exporter. But a government that allows its currency to float freely imposes a system of import control that is the most natural and effective. Indeed it is a perfect one. When the country is importing more than it is exporting, its currency is automatically devalued and the more it falls in value, the dearer its imports become, thus making its own products more competitive in the domestic market. At the same time they become more competitive in the world market since less of its country's currency must be purchased in the foreign exchange market in order to buy there. The converse is, of course, the case when a country's exports exceed its imports. The impersonal forces at work in the foreign exchanges make sure that the cost of importing its goods goes up.

Canada can supply us with as many thousands of tons of wheat as we would wish to have. That we would pay in Canadian dollars does not make it necessary for us to acquire the same amount of dollars by exporting to Canada goods that she might buy from us. If Canada could send us wheat cheaper than any other country, it would be to our advantage to buy it, regardless of whether Canada imported anything from us. The simple analogy is to be found in our everyday lives. To buy a joint of beef from the butcher we do not enquire whether he will engage our services or purchase whatever we may make in the course of our occupation. We buy his joint of beef because it is the cheapest or because his shop is the most convenient or because a neighbour recommended his meat, or for a mixture of those reasons; perhaps we buy from him because we met him in the local pub and enjoyed his company, perhaps because he is a fellow churchgoer, a fellow freemason or for a host of reasons, but the least likely reason is that he is in the habit of buying from us an equal amount of goods that we have for sale.

Of course, if the butcher buys his bread from a particular baker, the latter may reciprocate; the doctor also may have his house conveyed by the solicitor who is a patient, and the solicitor may have his car serviced by the mechanic who is his client. Those are exceptions to the rule: they illustrate that it is a blend of self-interest and sentiment, but mostly the former, that persuades us where to buy what we want. Trade across the seas and frontiers is carried on in precisely the same way. Just as we may buy all our meat from the butcher of our choice, regardless of whether he buys anything from us, so it matters not how much or how little another particular country buys from us. What does matter is that we should be able to buy our needs in the cheapest market. That is just what we cannot do when our trade policies are bedevilled by the balance of payment argument.

Any country that unilaterally declares a free trade policy and brings down all tariffs and other barriers to imports, irrespective of whether other countries reciprocate, will be taking an immense stride forward towards its own prosperity. Wealth in the real sense – goods that is, not cash in the modern form of intrinsically worthless pieces of paper – will pour in, and the people of that country will be set free to buy whatever they prefer. The country that permits its people more of that freedom than any other is Hong Kong. A country of scarcely any natural resources, densely and dangerously over-populated, producing only a fraction of its own food, Hong Kong yet succeeds in affording its people a level of prosperity that is the envy of the East.

To assert that free traders are against any import controls and that they are willing to see their country's industries unprotected is a mistake. They believe that just one kind of protection is necessary – an exchange rate that is allowed to float up and down without any interference by the government or central bank. The floating exchange rate is a mechanism that regulates the flow of imports and exports in the cheapest way possible and to a degree that each individual industry deserves.

Paper money cannot be eaten, it cannot be worn or provide shelter or energy. It has but one use: to be a means of buying something in the land where it belongs. Every pound sterling 'lost' in the so-called balance of payments is a pound spent, sooner or later, in this country. It will go towards paying for one of our exports or for some capital investment here. It must be spent in Britain. The greater our deficit on the current or trading account in our balance of payments, the greater must the surplus be in the capital entering Britain.

A sensible Government need never worry about the balance of payments, still less bother the people with the topic. It allows its currency to float cleanly – that is, without interfering by spending taxpayers' money in the foreign exchange market. Thus is provided a self-regulating mechanism that automatically corrects the volume of our exports and imports.

The harder we work, the more efficient and inventive we are, the greater the volume of imports the mechanism will permit. And imports, let it be emphasised, consist of wealth entering the country to raise the standard of living of the people. The converse follows: the less industrious and efficient we are, the more the same mechanism will require us to export – to lose wealth. Those who argue that we must not import food from abroad because of the balance of payments fail to see this difference between wealth in the true sense and paper money.

9/Conserving the Countryside

A prosperous agriculture will ensure the beauty of the countryside; impoverish farmers and the rural scene will look neglected and forlorn. This is the call that has come to the fore in the last few years to catch the spirit of the times. It is intended, no doubt, to enlist the support of the conservationists and environmentalists, and of that growing number of riders, ramblers, and motorists who desert the towns and suburbs to seek recreation in the countryside. There is an obvious link between the prosperity of the farmer and the beauty where he lives and works. I do not try to challenge that. However, I believe we should examine how the present support policies have affected the appearance of the countryside, and also whether there is not an alternative policy that would be more effective in safeguarding its beauties and amenities.

The countryside has, without a doubt, changed enormously in the last three decades. Changes have taken place especially in those areas which are farmed; and the more intensively an area has been farmed, the more the local countryside has changed. Even those sturdy souls who stride across Dartmoor, Exmoor and even Snowdonia discover sights and sounds which would never have been there in the late 1940s and early 1950s. A Forestry Commission, state-controlled and heavily subsidised by the long-suffering taxpayer, has acquired many thousands of acres and planted upon them a dark green vastness of conifers; sheep have also multiplied since import duties have been imposed on lamb from New Zealand, and substantial grants to pay for drainage, fencing and the reclamation of marginal land have had the effect of reducing the area of moorland. Yet the visitor returning after thirty years still recognises the scene; he knows it remains Dartmoor or Allendale.

But what of the visitor to the village of his birth anywhere

South of the Trent? The more agriculture has 'prospered', the more far-reaching the changes that the visitor will see after an absence of thirty years. As he approaches the village he will notice fewer hedgerows; many will have been up-rooted altogether, and many others have been replaced by barbed-wire fencing. Millions of pounds of public money have been responsible for this; grants to pay for the removal of hedgerows and further grants to pay for the barbed-wire fencing for which the farmer can receive 25 per cent of the cost. Such fencing is 'economic'; it enables livestock to be kept in more effectively; and it does not need many men-hours spent upon cutting it once a year; it enables every square inch to be grazed; and the plough gains another two feet around the field.

Our observant friend will also see many fewer trees and scarcely any within the field itself – such trees were useful when stock farming predominated, but are a nuisance to the arable farmer. It is likely that more than half the fields will now be arable, at least twice as many as he remembered before the war when the policy of minimal state control tilted the balance in favour of livestock. Does arable land look more pleasing to the eye than green pastures? The visitor must decide that for himself.

Then the visitor drives past the farmhouse. The old barns are gone. Some were built of local stone, others of elm and thatch; but only a few survive now. They were large enough for the old farmer, but government grants have subsidised the amalgamation of farms, so now it is necessary to have new buildings erected two or three times the size of the old ones. These new structures are made of concrete; they are efficient and sensible, but scarcely objects of breath-taking beauty. Two companies specialise in erecting them throughout the country; so wherever our visitor goes he will see the same uniform buildings and the same standardised materials. Again, substantial grants and generous tax allowances have speeded up the process of replacing the old with the new.

The eye of our observant friend will catch the sight of a pond where he used to stalk the newts, but now it seems to have a different shape. No wonder. The owner was given a government grant to fill it in, but after that particular scheme ended in March 1972, a 'Save the Ponds' Campaign was introduced and the owner took advantage of the help which was made available to dig it out again and to restore its previous usefulness.

Next our visitor will be surprised to see a huge factory beside one of the farms. How was planning permission granted? It has to be explained to him that planning laws are quite different for the farmers – they are, in the real sense of the word, privileged. Although it looks identical to a factory in an industrial estate, it is, in fact, called a cowtel. Inside, a herd of some two hundred dairy cows live their lives. Some are upstairs and some down. Much of their food is stored under the same roof and their milk is treated and pasteurised there as well. Our visitor may gaze in awe at its massive size and, if he is a trifle eccentric, at its beauty too. Should he be a taxpayer he might also contemplate how much he has contributed to its cost.

Yet it is in the country village itself where the transformation has come about. The village where I live is said to be the least changed in the whole county: its population is now 135, while thirty years ago it was 125. And only a few new houses have been built in those years. The difference is in the occupations of those who live there. Instead of ten full-time farmers, employing between them fourteen farm workers, there are now five; and only one employs full-time help. Most of the farm houses and cottages have been taken over by people who travel miles away (up to sixty miles) to work.

The farms have not changed much in size, but what they produce has. The emphasis used to be on dairying, six of the farmers being almost wholly dependent upon a monthly cheque from the Milk Marketing Board for their incomes, and each of them did quite well. None of them could now. Some fifteen years ago a dairy farm of eighty acres could support a milking herd of twenty cows and the farmer could afford to employ a full-time herdsman. The pastures were not overstocked, and feed stuffs were bought in on only a small scale. In a short space of time, such farming has been made quite unprofitable. It is not because wages have risen disproportionately; farmworkers' incomes have not, in fact, kept pace with those of industrial workers. Nor can it be because of 'cheap imports'. None of the usual explanations can point to the reason why our farms have been denuded of men who used to work on them. The finger must be pointed at the system that has made it worthwhile for the farmer to replace his men with machines.

Farm workers have left the land since then. Of course, the movement to the towns from the land has been going on for centuries, but now the picture is a different one. Former farm workers have tended to remain living in the villages and hamlets, and either new jobs have been brought to the country areas or the men have gone by the day to work in the country towns. It is this that has utterly transformed the scene in our old market towns and country villages.

As work was lost on the land so it was found in hundreds of new small industries – and some not so small – that have been established in our country towns and villages. Anyone travelling through counties such as Wiltshire or Suffolk, whose fortunes were once entirely wrapped up in agriculture, can see how many new factories have been built since the war, and every one on what used to be farming land, on the outskirts of the towns. In Wiltshire, for example, the towns of Marlborough, Devizes, Melksham, Bradford-on-Avon, Chippenham, Calne, Warminster and Westbury were, some thirty years ago, redolent of rurality. Any customer in a shop was as likely as not to be a farmer or his wife or a farm worker or his wife. The townspeople felt themselves to be part of the agricultural scene, for most of them had jobs that in some way or another were serving agriculture. They talked farming; when it rained or the sun shone down, their thoughts were on how it would affect the farmers. Bank managers, solicitors, accountants, and other professional people went out of their way to keep abreast of the farming problems to an extent that is no longer essential. In a local newspaper market news and farming features were given prominence, for every editor knew what his readers wanted.

The other two towns in Wiltshire, Salisbury and Swindon, had further interests, the Army and the Church in one and the Great Western Railway in the other, yet the concern for agriculture in them both was still apparent to anyone coming to those towns for the first time.

A very different impression would now be gained by our visitor. Not one in twenty of the customers in the shops in any of those towns would be a farmer or farm worker or their wives. In fact, of Wiltshire's half-million population, only 2 per cent are now in agriculture. Each town has attracted one or more industries that have no associations with farming. The affinity with farming has not gone completely, but it is insignificant compared with what it used to be.

What has been true of Wiltshire equally applies to all the counties of England, where thirty years ago the influence of agriculture was supreme. My own constituency, Holland-with-Boston, is the only one in England which might be an exception; but, regrettably, under the reform of local government, Holland has ceased to be a separate county. There are a few parts of Wales where you can feel the same influence and also in Scotland, but the more rural the area the greater the chance of tourism superseding agriculture.

Physically and outwardly all these old market towns have changed. Market squares are taken over by supermarkets and chain stores; the Corn Exchanges by a bingo hall; scarcely a single cattle market survives in the centre of any town. The country towns have become industrialised, not completely of course, but enough to stop them being the local centre of agriculture. Each one of them, without exception, is larger than it used to be; many of them are twice or three times their previous size. As they have sprawled out, gobbling up green pastures and rural lanes, they have done nothing to enhance the beauty that used to be there.

There need be no mystery why this has happened. Businessmen wanting to expand or begin a new venture have sought out the place where labour costs were comparatively low. When an industry sheds as many of its employees as agriculture has done, there is a vacuum to be filled. In the conditions of full employment that prevailed for more than two decades, businessmen had little choice but to move out into these country towns, and often the villages as well.

The new industries needed wider, straighter, faster roads to connect the old country towns and villages with rail heads and motorways and directly with the cities and conurbations. Many a country lane has had to change to accommodate this new traffic. This demand for speedy communication for heavy goods vehicles has brought changes to the countryside, over some twenty years, that conservationists have had to accept with regret. Villages on the routes of this traffic have suffered in obvious ways, but so far it has not been obvious how the fabric and structure of many ancient cottages and manor houses have been damaged by the vibration of these heavy lorries. If my reasoning as to why these new industries have come to the countryside is even partially right, it will be quite impossible to calculate how much of the beauty of our countryside, of our country towns and of our villages has been lost by a policy that has caused so many men to lose their jobs on the land and to be replaced by machines subsidised by the taxpayer.

It is true that these changes on the farms may convey an impression of cleanliness and orderliness. It may well be admired. Look more carefully to see what has been done and one finds that a tribute must be paid to the herbicides and pesticides and fungicides that liberally dose our land. The weeds have gone; thistles, nettles, docks need no longer be part of the landscape, but many a wild flower has gone with them.

The farmers remain the custodians of the countryside. We cannot expect them to discharge that role when it conflicts with their economic interests, for we have to confess that aesthetics and economics are not, unfortunately, close relations. If farmers are to protect the beauty of the countryside, the general public must be ready to compensate them financially whenever this conflict arises. This principle has already been established by the Field Monument Act, 1972. The farmer who has, for example, an ancient barrow in a field that he intends to plough up can receive a grant from the Government to make good the pecuniary loss he suffers by protecting it. It has been extended by the Wild Life and Countryside Act, 1981.

There seems to be no reason why this principle should not be extended now to the landscape generally. If a farmer believes it is necessary to cut down trees or uproot a hedgerow, fill in a pond, demolish a thatched barn, or pull down a stone wall in order to maintain the profitability of his holding, it should be possible to apply for a grant by way of compensation for

83

maintaining that feature on the landscape. Members of the valuers' profession are already invited to compute a capital sum for wayleaves, compensation for road-making schemes, and other occasions when the Land Compensation Act is invoked, so it would not be an intractable problem to assess the basis of these new grants.

As to the appropriate agency, the Ministry of Agriculture, the County Councils or the Countryside Commission, each has an existing interest in this area, although perhaps the latter might be the most appropriate. If there is any fear that the grants might be distributed unevenly or arbitrarily, a fairly simple procedure could be devised to enable appeals to be made to the Lands Tribunal. The justification for such a system of landscape amenity grants seems to be beyond doubt. In the first place the farmer is running a business, and it must pay its way. Secondly, the general public, on the other hand, can be assumed to wish to see the beauty of the countryside and to pay some small premium to have it safeguarded. Neither of those conditions now prevails; in both cases they are only half true. I return to this point in Chapter 10 to show that this policy would be more advantageous to our hill farmers than the present method of protection.

Let us be clear about one essential fact. The farmer may be running a business, but *it* does not pay – the general public pays. The public may wish to see the beauty of the countryside, yet it continues to pay the premium not to safeguard it, but to put it in constant jeopardy.

The Future

10/The Free Trade Alternative

As someone who has been both farmer and politician, I am wholly prejudiced in favour of the former. In the next chapter I have tried to show that farmers have nothing to fear by being separated from politicians and (which is really the same) from being freed from state control and government intervention. But, unfortunately, not many farmers realise that protectionism is itself a form of state control; and once politicians are asked to protect an industry other forms of intervention always follow.

It is another unfortunate fact that only a minority of farmers seem to appreciate that the surest foundation for their own prosperity is the economic strength and well-being of the whole country. If Britain and the British people prosper so too will British farmers. Perhaps the converse applies still more. When Britain's fortunes decline and the British people suffer a fall in their standard of living, that is the time when British farmers will also cease to flourish. Certain spokesmen for the NFU and several agricultural commentators are blind to that simple proposition. If they persist in speaking and writing on the contrary premise, they will do infinite harm in widening the gulf between farmers and the rest of the British people.

So let us look, first of all, at what is the interest of the British people – or indeed the people of any nation – as individuals. The banal truth is that they should buy in the cheapest market and sell in the dearest. All of us depart from that principle at various times. Our neighbour who is a pork butcher may get our custom as an act of friendly neighbourliness, although his sausages may be a trifle more expensive. A former prisoner of war of the Japanese may flinch from buying a Datsun. Sentiment may play a part when we buy anything: we pay a premium then for expressing our feelings. Nevertheless, it remains in our interest economically to buy the sausages or the car we like at the cheapest price.

And what goes for individuals goes for nations too. There is no difference. Individuals trade – nations do not, apart from a few totalitarian exceptions. International trade is thus a false term; trade takes place between individuals, who may happen to live and do their business in different parts of the world. Those individuals may, of course, be acting as employees of great corporations or small firms, or on their own account. Their particular status does not matter. Whether or not they are trading in their own name, it is still their job; and the rewards they receive will reflect how well they do that job. The cheaper they buy, and the dearer they sell, the better their reward.

Any system of protection is an attempt to lessen those rewards. In the case of agriculture every single device that can be used to support agriculture is a form of protection. All subsidies serve to protect agriculture, grants for fencing and fertiliser are intended to give British farmers an advantage to compete with other farmers, and thus to exclude their produce from entering Britain. Providing free advice by ADAS, which costs the taxpayer about £400 per British farmer, has the same object. Tariffs, duties, levies, and quotas, are the obvious forms of protection, but the other forms of support are just as damaging to trade and, because they are concealed and insidious, are likely to prevent trade taking place without potential buyers appreciating their impact.

Protection is indeed prevention. It prevents the trade in those commodities that can be produced in the home market. Now the protectionist sees nothing wrong in that, for he is apt to regard every import as a kind of invasion that should be repulsed. It is as if there is an enemy at the gate who is bombarding us, and the citizens within must be protected from the missiles. What are these dangerous missiles? They are nothing more than the food, the goods, and the raw materials that the British people want to buy and have the money to pay for. The exporter to Britain is a willing seller; the importer in Britain is a willing buyer. Thus every act of protection is an attempt by the state to stand between a willing seller and a willing buyer.

According to what principles has the state the right to intervene in that way and encroach upon the freedom of them both? The answers that are given by the farming lobby I have sought to rebut in the previous chapters, but the question needs to be repeated for it underlines the moral issue. Free trade is as much a moral as an economic issue. Going back to man's beginning, to what political philosophers call the state of nature, whether a man hunted or fished, whether he made rough tools or primitive clothes, he wished to exchange his surplus produce with others who had something to give in return. From that simple process of exchange all man's mighty achievements have flowed. So long as there was no state to interfere, man's freedom to trade was only limited by natural obstacles, such as the distance he travelled in search of others to trade with.

As man overcame nature's obstacles, so his wealth increased. That is what economic history is about. Comparing the life of primitive man – what he ate, where he slept, what clothes he wore and how he kept himself warm – with life of man, say, just a century ago, one realises that thousands of years went by without anything like the enormous changes that have occurred since then. Nature no longer stands in the way of our having a vast range of mechanical aids and nearly every part of them may be made from metal which has been brought thousands of miles to Britain. Nature no longer stands in our way as we fly to New York in a few hours. Nature does not stand in our way when we want to heat our homes at a moment's notice. Nature does not stand in our way when we choose to eat the food of other soils and climates at a price, thanks to modern transportation, that is only a little above what it may cost in the country of its origin.

But the state does! The obstacles of nature which have in the past made such moves prohibitively expensive are replaced by obstacles of the state which made them as prohibitively expensive as they used to be. To underline this power of prohibition by the state, let us take four specific examples:

(1) New Zealand can produce cheese cheaper than any other country in the world. Until this century, the obstacles of nature made it impossible for the British people to eat it, but once they were able to do so their economic well-being was improved and

one of their wants satisfied. Protectionism has now phased out this supply and if we want to eat cheese we are required by law to eat other kinds which are much more expensive. Our economic well-being has diminished accordingly.

(2) Canada can offer us tinned salmon cheaper than any other country. As with New Zealand cheese, the obstacles of nature prevented the British people having the salmon until this century. But after they were able to buy it another of their wants was satisfied. High tariffs have changed all that: tinned salmon is now a luxury item.

(3) There is probably no country in the world better suited for ranching beef cattle than Argentina. Nature's obstacles in enabling us to have this supply are gone; and none did more to remove them than British businessmen. But the British people are now prohibited from eating this beef, first of all by a total embargo, and now by prohibitively high tariffs.

(4) Australia used to send us considerable quantities of butter and fruit. When the first shiploads came in they were heralded as a remarkable achievement. Now no Australian butter can enter Britain and her fruit is made so expensive by tariffs that we can have only a little of it.

Numerous other examples can be given. Those are enough to establish two features of protectionism. The first is that it is economically and commercially reactionary. It puts the clock back. It undoes the good that man has done to overcome the difficulties of supplying our needs. It denies and countermands progress. What is the point of investing in refrigeration and building fleets of ships equipped to carry vast quantities of food to these shores in a way which would have been impossible in the lifetime of our grandparents, if the state is to intervene and decree that we are not to take advantage of such economic progress? And is it sensible for a young dairy farmer to go to New Zealand to take over a holding in the most suitable area in the world for dairying if he is to be denied a market for what he can produce?

The second feature of protectionism is that it is an act of coercion. Sometimes it imposed a total prohibition, as with beef from Australia and Argentina. Here are two countries so happily blessed by nature that they can produce beef more

90

cheaply than anywhere else. Yet during the time of that embargo any meat trader in Britain who imported that cheap meat would have committed a criminal offence. He would have stood in the dock and been punished as if he had been guilty of shoplifting. At the very same time hundreds of farmers in both Australia and Argentina were going out of business – unable to sell their cattle!

Even when, as is usually the case, protectionism takes the form of tariffs or quotas, the element of coercion is still present. The importer must pay the duty prescribed and his failure to do so constitutes a crime. Equally, where quotas are imposed to restrict the quantity he can import, should he exceed the quota he also commits a crime. As to the subsidies and grants, any taxpayer who objects to these being paid to farmers and withholds part of his income tax in protest, would be guilty of an offence under the Income Tax Acts.

Protectionists may dislike the use of such words being introduced into the argument. To speak of crimes and coercion is emotive, they protest. Unfortunately, they do not seem to understand that they are trampling upon a freedom which concerns the British people every day of their lives. Our freedom to trade governs our standard of living and decides, in the case of food, what we eat at every meal.

The 'British' breakfast, as it is called abroad, of bacon and eggs, has disappeared from millions of breakfast tables in the last few years, ever since protectionism more than doubled the cost of the pig producer's feeding stuffs. The 'British' Sunday dinner of roast beef and Yorkshire pudding is enjoyed now by a minority. The less well-off who used to have tinned salmon for tea followed by tinned peaches now make do with pastas. Continental cheeses and continental butter, both heavily subsidised, have taken the place of cheese from Canada, Australia and New Zealand, which are intended to be permanently taxed at such a high level as to be excluded from our homes. The hard wheats of North America for our bread bear a tax that effectively doubles their price, so that the former standby for every hungry family has had its consumption cut by a quarter.

These changes on our tables have not come about by the free

choice of the British people, but because of tariffs, quotas and other devices of protectionism. None of these devices could be made to work unless the state used its sanctions to enforce them. And each sanction depends upon the powers of the police, the customs officers and the criminal courts – indeed ultimately the jail house. In other words, remove these sanctions and freedom of trade will be restored. Importers would then be free to buy from abroad the kind of food they believe the British housewife would wish to have, and accordingly she would be able to place upon the table once again the meals that her family would like to eat.

In conditions of free trade businessmen conduct their affairs on simple commercial principles. Whether their sales and purchases are entirely in the home market or entirely abroad or, more likely, a mixture of both, they seek to buy and sell as profitably as they can in the knowledge that each transaction is with a willing partner, who is as free as he is himself to buy and sell. Whether the businessman is a small shopkeeper in a remote village or head of a great company that trades throughout the world, there is no difference in the principle; small shopkeepers cannot compel the housewives to buy and the great company cannot force a sale. Whatever the size of the business it must provide the customer with what he or she wants to have and can afford to pay for. Failure to do so opens a door for the competitor who will satisfy the customer's freedom of choice. Free trade is thus commercial democracy.

Protectionism can be called, without exaggeration, commercial authoritarianism. The best that can be said for it is that it extends a benign paternalism over the realm of commerce. You must not buy a toffee apple from the shop in the next village, it's a nasty cheap one; go and buy a lovely lollipop from the nice gentleman who keeps a shop in our road. Most intrusions upon the freedom of man begin in a benign, paternal way. At first, admonition rather than punishment follows those who err from the ordained path, but there soon comes a time when sterner steps have to be taken to ensure obedience. That is why a mere 'Buy British' campaign, although sentiment may afford it some marginal success, will never be the basis of a support policy for agriculture.

92

The result is that, when protectionism prevails, the businessman can no longer conduct his affairs on simple commercial principles. Politics intervene. It is politicians who decide which items are to be protected, and how much protection each is to have. These are decisions that make or break a business. Any businessman who made his living by importing into Britain Australian butter and cheese – to quote but one example – has been forced to look for other work to do. Manufacturers of high-cost butter and cheese in Britain and other countries in the EEC have taken his place. It is not for nothing that nearly all the very large companies in Britain today have a 'Government Affairs' Department, either under that name or another. Within a mile or two of Whitehall one can find scores of offices rented by a wide variety of companies who regard it as essential to have a post near 'where the action is'. A Member of Parliament or a retired civil servant need have no particular skills to be invited to work for their companies as a consultant. While it is true that much of this activity is due to the amount of legislation that steadily increases the power of government over business life, nevertheless it is protectionism that has made it commercially necessary.

A few years ago a small firm in my constituency that supplied fertilisers to hundreds of farmers in the East Midlands received an offer from a German company to sell them a fertiliser at a favourable price. The offer was accepted, but before the first shipload arrived at Boston Docks, an anti-dumping order was made and the ship had to return to Germany. The order was made in Whitehall at the request of a famous large UK company that was competing with the small firm among the farmers in the East Midlands, but it could never have been made with such speed if the company had not had a government affairs department presided over by a skilful operator, who was on Christian name terms with the civil servants responsible and whom he was known to take out to lunch at his club at regular intervals. (Being a member of the same club, I am able to bear witness to it.)

Protectionism mixes up trade with politics. Up to a point it may not matter very much. A few small businessmen may get hurt and the British people lose a part of their freedom. But

93

protectionism never stands still for long. It is either waxing or waning. Allowed to wax, the dangers are desperately serious. Economists used to say, 'When goods cannot cross frontiers, armies will'. Protectionism is more than chauvinism; it is aggression. Chauvinism can be expressed as a preference for buying a British car or refusing to buy a Japanese television set; it is a negative attitude that can change when the price is lowered. Putting up tariffs and quotas against another country is, however, a positive act of aggression which cannot be put right by the exporter lowering his price.

Any kind of aggression, whether between individuals or nations, must give rise to friction and mistrust. When people of different countries trade freely with one another their interests converge; and the more they trade together the more those interests merge together. The prospect of conflict between them diminishes and gradually fades away altogether. This, after all, was one of the motives that brought France and Germany together at the Messina Conference, which led to the creation of the Common Market. Schuman, Spaak, Monnet, Adenauer, Hallstein, Pineau, Luns were, according to the preamble to the Treaty of Rome, 'determined to lay the foundation of an ever-closer union among the peoples of Europe, resolved to ensure the economic and social progress of their countries by common action to eliminate the barriers which divide Europe.'

They knew that artificial trade barriers set up by one nation against another are a source of commercial frustration. Allowed to persist, the frictions they cause develop into conflict. The Founding Fathers of the EEC were at heart free traders. Sadly, their child has gone awry.

The idea of Imperial Preference was substantially the same. Trade can only be carried on between people who are communicating together; by giving them the fullest possible commercial opportunities to communicate together – for that is implicit when there is complete free trade – any misunderstanding and mistrust that might otherwise exist must diminish. Distances across the oceans disappear. A commercial cohesion develops into a mutual loyalty and a regard for the interests of each other. It has been said that war does not break out between nations that are trading together freely. If this is a fact of economic history, it must be the supreme monument raised up in the cause of free trade.

It is inconceivable that Argentina would have invaded the Falkland Islands if Britain had remained the most important market for her exports of beef and wheat, as was the case before we entered the Common Market. Her prosperity had been built up and was dependent upon that trade. By prohibiting her exports Britain caused a large proportion of the Argentinian people to suffer grievous hardship and many thousands to lose their jobs. In due course, Soviet Russia moved in to take Britain's place as Argentina's principal trading partner; and in so doing she saved her from economic disaster.

The cost to the British people of protecting agriculture and other industries is much the same as the cost of maintaining our defence services. Defence against whom? Soviet Russia may be the obvious answer, but taking the longer view the danger lies in a conflict between North and South. The South – the Third World – becomes remorselessly more impoverished as each decade moves into the next. Ideological missionaries from Havana spread the word that their country provides every citizen with a job and a house and that the old extremes of affluence and poverty have given way to a fair distribution of Cuba's wealth. But the pith and core of their message is that the prosperity of the Cuban people has come about by turning away from the West and severing the trading links that have existed with Europeans and North Americans. This, they tell the people of Africa, South America and the Caribbean, is the corner-stone of their policy. Trade with Russia and Comecon countries: they will treat you fairly, as comrades do, but do not trade with those who have exploited you ever since you traded beyond your frontiers. These missionaries in the cause of Communism go on to point to the Lomé Convention between the EEC and the Third World, and mock its hypocrisy. The tariffs come down, they say, but look at the quotas and the other barriers that go up to prevent you exporting to Western Europe. Oh yes, they add, the West will lend you money, but notice the strings attached. In all this there is, sadly, more than just a grain of truth.

Agriculture: The Triumph and the Shame

If the opponents of free trade wish to dispute this thesis, they must be sure of two matters. The first is that our protectionism is not adversely affecting those countries of the Third World and that it is in their interest to submit to our protectionist policy. The second is that a poor country, becoming poorer, is not susceptible to the tuition of the Communist ideologues.

The potential of the Third World countries to feed both themselves and so much of the developed West, especially ourselves, is enormous. They have great advantages of soil and climate, and we can export to them the necessary skills and the capital. There is no need to prove the capacity of the developed Commonwealth countries, of New Zealand, Canada, and Australia especially. I hope that enough has already been written in this book to show how much we have cut off the trading links with them. The cohesion and loyalties those links reinforced for so long are now in danger. Because agricultural protectionism has hurt those countries, there is a distance between us which is more than geographical. The defence of the West is the loser.

There is little evidence that our Victorian forebears worried about war. The literature and the architecture they have bequeathed to us – indeed almost everything they left us – assumed that the nation's peace need not be disturbed. Some of them used to drink a toast: 'Peace and Free Trade with all the World'. It was not only historians and economists who had perception enough to see the connection. A new generation of businessmen, exporting and importing for the first time, realised then what has ceased to be obvious to us now. It is that when free trade prevails, the seller is not forced to sell nor the buyer to buy, so that all trade that is carried on must be to the benefit of both; and as the trade gathers pace, so do the benefits multiply. And they will continue to multiply so long as the people live in peace.

Of course, free trade throughout the world is a pipe dream. The British people, however, can insist that their country should set an example and declare the ports of Britain open. What other country would be so foolish as to deny to people the advantage offered? What country would hate us or fear us for doing that? Nothing could do more to secure peace for the British people than a unilateral declaration for free trade.

96

Timorous souls will let out the oft-repeated cry that we will be flooded with imports. They can be reassured. The more imports the better; they will enter our ports only to the extent that we can afford them. A flood of imports will be a measure of our prosperity, and as was pointed out earlier, a floating exchange rate is all we will need to prevent the flood getting out of control. It will in fact provide a particularly effective defence for agriculture, since it works by influencing the prices of different goods, and agriculture is very adaptable. It may sometimes find it costly to change from one crop to another but it can make the switch more quickly than any other industry. This is especially true of the arable sector.

So far as agriculture is concerned, the free trader would accept that there are three ways in which imports might be restricted. The first is action against dumping. When all exporting of food was in the hands of private enterprise, this was not a danger, but now that numerous governments, especially the Communist governments and the Commission of the EEC, engage in interstate trading with the aid of massive sums of taxpayers' money, there are new factors that must be taken into account. This kind of dumping of food may be a political and hostile act done with the intention of undermining another country's capacity to grow food. In those circumstances, measures to resist it can be a justifiable part of our system of national defence.

It may also be desirable to limit certain imports as a result of modern technology. Rapid growth can be stimulated by adding arsenic, copper and hormones to animal feeds. Producers have found that pigs and chicken, when given these supplements, reach maturity several weeks earlier, and if their use were forbidden, meat would become substantially more expensive. Antibiotics are also used on a considerable scale by intensive producers; and again, without their use, the price of meat would have to rise.

On the other hand, these practices involve dangers to our health. To forbid their use would put our farmers at a disadvantage if similar restrictions were not imposed on foreign competitors, and as matters now stand, nearly all these additives can be used quite freely, although some limits may be imposed by the European Community. Arable farmers accustomed to applying herbicides, pesticides and fungicides should also be put on the same footing as foreign competitors.

So much evidence is being gathered against these practices that it may be feasible, in a few years' time, to hold an international conference to see whether an agreement could be reached to ban at least some of them. The FAO might be the appropriate body to organise it and to invite representatives from the government of every country engaged in exporting food. Once any agreement was reached, the different governments could then set about changing the law in each of their countries. Failing such an agreement, our own Parliament should take unilateral action. This would take the form of a ban upon a particular kind of food being imported from a country that permitted it to be produced in a way that we had forbidden.

The third permissible interference was touched on in the last chapter. Our countryside is a beautiful heritage, but the trees, hedges, ponds, thatched barns and stone walls that are a part of our island's beauty do not always make for economic farm management. Hence there is a case for extending the principle in the Field Monument Act, 1972, of giving farmers grants for preserving certain features that they would like to sweep away.

There is no conflict between a free trade policy and giving grants to the owners or occupiers of the countryside for the purpose of maintaining the beauty of the landscape. Such a system of landscape grants would, above all, benefit the farmers who now own or occupy our marginal land. They are the custodians of much of our most beautiful landscape. Tens of thousands of them now earn a precarious livelihood, despite the many millions of pounds that are diverted into supporting high-cost livestock production that should be to their advantage. In fact, if a mere fraction of those vast sums were to be paid directly to them, they would be financially much better off.

Thus, such grants would cost the taxpayer considerably less than he is now required to pay and the marginal farmer could receive an income higher than he does at present. But his actual farming activities might be curtailed: his high-cost food would have a smaller place in the market. Instead of impoverishing his fellow-countrymen, which the present system frankly makes him do, he will be enriching the beauty of the land.

11/When British Farming Flourished

The great Lord Melbourne summed up the views of many landowners and farmers, before the Corn Laws were repealed, in words that would be echoed today: 'To leave the whole agricultural interest without protection, I declare before God that I think it the wildest and maddest scheme that has ever entered into the imagination of men to conceive.'

Thus he thundered, no doubt in profound sincerity, but how mistaken he was proved to be! Those who speak in the same language as Lord Melbourne in this century are also mistaken, but for reasons that are somewhat different. Circumstances have, without question, changed; but not all of them have and the facts of today are the foundation for fresh arguments why farmers should give their support to a free trade policy.

First, let us establish two facts and in doing so bury two myths of history. The first fact is that farmers prospered exceedingly after the Corn Laws were repealed. The second is that farmers in the inter-war period of 1918-1939 were somewhat better off than the rest of the nation.

The protectionist lobby and the pressure groups campaigning for agricultural expansion, which are supported by the major companies servicing agriculture, have worked hard ever since the last war to create myths to the contrary. And they have been successful. Almost every farmer and every agricultural journalist or commentator is of the opinion now that agricultural depression coincides with free trade. The general view among all the many people who take a sympathetic interest in agriculture, although not themselves engaged in farming, is the same. One could go further and say that it has become self-evident to them all that agriculture's fortunes must decline in conditions of free trade, and the longer liberal trade policies are pursued the further the decline will go on.

Even taxpayers' money has been used to further the myth. The Central Office of Information published a booklet after the war, *Prospect for the Land*, in which it spoke of agriculture between the wars as a 'neglected, almost bankrupt industry.' The British Council in a booklet entitled *British Agriculture* spoke of the inter-war years as being the 'Black Years' – using capital letters to register its point – for British agriculture.

The historic campaign that led to the repeal of the Corn Laws enlisted the vigorous support of thousands of landowners and farmers who did not share the Cassandra-like judgment of Lord Melbourne. Richard Cobden had himself been a farmer's son and throughout his life he maintained an interest in agriculture. If John Bright lacked that background, Edward Baines, the most prolific of the writers in the campaign, was a farmer as well as a newspaper editor; and Mr Villiers, the MP for Wolverhampton for over half a century and for many years the lone voice in the House of Commons for free trade, was also associated with farming. Great landowners like the Earl of Radnor, Earl Fitzwilliam, Lord Nugent, Lord Morpeth and the Earl of Ducie, whose fortunes were dependent on agriculture's well being, joined the campaign.

Then there were the smaller farmers: many had attended the meetings held by William Cobbett, two decades previously, as he stumped the country writing his *Rural Rides* and addressing large audiences of farmers, evening after evening. There has never been such a doughty champion of the farmer, nor such a wordsmith to lambast London – 'the Great Wen' – and all its works to such effect. His pungent scorn for anyone or anything standing in the way of the farmer getting his just reward lives on immortally in the pages of *Rural Rides*. And he, of course, was a free trader.

The case he advanced against the Corn Laws in a speech in Sussex, on 3 January 1822, reported in his *Rural Rides*, could be repeated word for word today to show that the restriction or prohibition of imported food does not serve the interests of agriculture. He himself had tried to persuade his fellow farmers to petition against the first Corn Bill, but failed to secure a single other supporter. Among the arguments he put to them was 'a Bill could do us no good, while it would not fail to excite against us the ill-will of the other classes of the community; a thought by no means pleasant.' In reminding his audience in Sussex of that, he declared 'Thus it has been.' If farmers, especially tenants, are concerned today at the effect of inflation, Cobbett spent much of his time in the 1820s denouncing the 'boundless issue of paper money' as the real enemy of agriculture, not free trade. (If any farmer could equal his fervour in this century it would be the late A.G. Street, author of *Farmer's Glory* and numerous other evocative books about the countryside, who was known to millions of radio listeners: he also was a free trader.) The anti-Corn Law campaigners, as they went from market town to market town, rekindled the dying flames that were the message left behind by Cobbett. By the time repeal came, there were many areas where the majority of farmers were as much in favour of free trade as were the spinners and weavers of Lancashire.

The Act repealing the Corn Laws was passed in 1846, but there was a three-year period of transition in which the duties were gradually reduced, with the result that from February 1849 there was only a nominal duty of one shilling a quarter imposed upon imported corn. Then followed thirty years of prosperity for British agriculture. Thousands of farm houses were demolished to make way for larger and more opulent homes; the children were sent away for a private education; the daughters were given piano lessons and the sons ponies to ride. The farmers themselves were now to be seen riding in the hunting field or trotting off in dog carts for a day's shooting; the wives were going to the most expensive dressmakers in the market towns and, at home, were leaving the kitchen to the servants so that they might spend their hours in the new drawing room entertaining friends and neighbours. A social gap developed between farmer and farm worker; the latter now ceased to live in and eat his meals as one of the family. Instead he had a home of his own, married young, and was given a wage substantially higher.

All this is chronicled and is not to be gainsaid. Many a Victorian novel conveys an accurate picture of this prosperity. So do the Probate records that tell us how much money farmers left compared with their fathers. So do the local newspapers of the time in giving the details of farm sales and market prices. These and other annals have been drawn upon by historians who have all reached the same conclusion about the state of agriculture after thirty years of free trade.

Let one quotation suffice. It is from an article in the *Encyclopaedia Britannica*. It was written in 1875 and summarises in one sentence the happy state in which our farmers were: 'In closing this review of British agriculture it is gratifying and cheering to reflect that never was this branch of national industry in a healthier condition, and never was there such solid ground for anticipating for it a steady and rapid progress.'

The reason for this great prosperity in conditions of free trade is relevant to our present state. The repeal of the Corn Laws brought down the price of bread – an item that comprised the greatest part of the diet of the industrial worker and his family. His wage did not diminish, so that he had more money to spend than before. It is significant that he and his family then became meat eaters. Meat consumption rose rapidly in this period and reached a level, per head of the population, higher than it is today. This meat that was now in demand had to be produced on British farms for it was not practical to import it on any scale, unlike corn. Producing meat was more profitable than growing corn, and any loss that was borne by harvesting less corn was more than made good by the gain of grazing cattle and sheep for the butcher together with the rearing of pigs. Arable farming in East Anglia continued as before, but elsewhere it was giving way to an emphasis on livestock production.

A return to a policy of free trade would have similar consequences for us a century later. The British people would be immeasurably better off with protection removed. I hope earlier chapters of this book have established how massive is the burden of taxation and how enormous is the transfer of capital as a result of supporting agriculture. The raising of real incomes by what certainly would be 15 per cent and could be 25 per cent over a period of time, the rediversion of capital to the efficient industries of our country, and the consequent reduction in the present high level of unemployment would unquestionably bring to the British people a standard of living substantially higher than it is at the present time.

More money in the pockets and the purses of the British people would enable them to regain the eating habits that they have lost. The figures in Chapter 12, showing how much less we are eating, demonstrates the point. Beef on Sundays again! Bacon for breakfast again!

The years 1846 to 1879 illustrate well enough that when a nation prospers, so do its farmers. The history of any nation, through its periods of prosperity and adversity, will confirm this fact and raise it to the dignity of an economic law. And the converse must also be true. There lies the danger to British farmers in arguing in favour of the present policy which is – if the evidence in this book is true – gradually sending Britain and the British people into a state of economic decline.

1879 was, as every student of our agricultural history knows, the year when arable farming went into decline. Throughout the summer and autumn the rain persisted; harvesting was impossible, and by November the arable fields were covered with nothing better than rotten corn. In 1880 it again rained continuously, although this time some of the crops were gathered in.

These two disastrous years coincided with an agricultural revolution in the United States, Canada and Australia. Their great wheat-growing areas were being opened up by the railroad, and steamships were now available to transport the corn across the ocean in large quantities, speedily and cheaply. The tractor was soon to follow; and Messrs Massey-Harris and McCormick were in due course to bring to the farmers of North America and Australia machines that were to transform the whole process of harvesting, making it possible to reap and thresh at a fraction of what it had cost before.

The British farmer, especially in England, still held fast to mixed farming with most of his land under plough. The four-year rotation was the alpha and omega of what he considered to be the right use of his land. His father had believed it to be so, so had his grandfather; all his neighbours were of the same mind; and the pundits who sat at their desks, as they do today, and wrote their books on the science of agriculture, did not deviate from this accepted wisdom.

As the 1880s gave way to the 1890s the incomes of these

farmers, in countless cases, were transformed into losses and bankruptcies. Farms were coming up for sale now and fetching less than they had done since the days of the Corn Laws. This was the situation throughout most of England; in the West Country and in counties like Northumberland, where the emphasis tended to be on livestock farming, the prosperity continued. So it did in Wales and Scotland, and for the same reason.

Quite a movement of farmers and of farmers' sons was now to be seen. As the farms of central and southern England came onto the market, so did the livestock-rearing Scotsmen, Welshmen, North Countrymen and West Countrymen arrive on the scene to take advantage of the opportunity to buy up these holdings and adapt them to the skills that they brought with them. Many a parish in central and southern England still has a Davies or a Jones, a Graham or a Stewart, whose forebears made such a journey.

Having bought these farms, they put them down to grass. Perhaps a few fields of oats or beans for feed, but the rest stayed green the whole year through. These were the men who survived the depression; the others gradually sold up, unless they followed the example of their new neighbours or had other sources of income. The depression did not descend on all agriculture, but upon the old-style arable farming – that agreeable, gentlemanly way of earning a livelihood that carried on despite the repeal of the Corn Laws, until others, with the advantage of a more favourable soil and climate, were able to provide the consumer with a supply of cheaper wheat. That other branch of agriculture that is concerned with producing livestock continued to expand, although not to such an extent as to prevent the total level of agricultural production from falling.

The 1914-18 War went a long way to reverse the trend. The price of wheat rose from 31 shillings a quarter to over 80 shillings; or, in other words, it was back to the price prevailing at the time of the Corn Laws, in the first half of the previous century. Thus, the enemy U-Boat served the same purpose and, in one sense, achieved the same result as the Corn Laws.

Once the Great War was over, the price fell again, and this time it gradually slithered down to 20 shillings a quarter in

1934. By this time the combine harvester was in general use in the great wheat-growing countries; their wheat did not have to be dried by any expensive process as in our own country; the vast prairies enabled economies of scale to be practised, not only in every facet of production but equally in its marketing.

The Wheat Act and the Import Duty Act, both passed in 1932, went some way to slow down the decline in our arable farming, yet despite these restrictions upon the free trade in wheat, so few farmers returned to this crop that by 1939 there were, throughout the whole of the United Kingdom, no more than 150 combine harvesters in use. That fact seems to indicate the small part wheat was able to play in our economy. Regionally, wheat was important in those areas of East Anglia where the good quality land will always make its growing sensible and profitable, whatever agricultural policy is pursued; and it was in East Anglia that nearly all those combine harvesters were to be found. Nationally, it was a different story.

Nonetheless, it is a myth that British agriculture was in a state of depression by the time the 1939-45 War began. Arable farming was indeed depressed; but in terms of capital investment, labour employed and production, it had been for many years of considerably less significance than the livestock sector. The latter flourished before the War – and flourished as much as any branch of our nation's trade and industry.

Despite the fall in arable production, total agricultural output rose. O. J. Beilby of the Agricultural Economic Research Institute of Oxford published an index of production that included every agricultural commodity. The years taken were from 1885 to 1936, and he made the years 1927-29 the base of 100. The startling result of his research is:

1885 – 1889	. . . . .	94
1890 – 1894	. . . . .	93
1895 – 1899	. . . . .	85
1900 – 1904	. . . . .	82
1905 – 1909	. . . . .	89
1910 – 1914	. . . . .	87
1915 – 1919	. . . . .	91
1922 – 1924	. . . . .	83

1925 – 1927	. . . . .	94
1927 – 1929	. . . . .	100
1928 – 1930	. . . . .	99
1931 – 1933	. . . . .	104
1934 – 1936	. . . . .	110

According to figures published subsequently by the Ministry of Agriculture, agriculture continued to expand and for 1939-40 production was 4.8 per cent more than in 1936. Mr Beilby's index shows that 1900-1904 was the lowest point to which output fell. By 1936 it had risen by no less than 34 per cent. Critics of our pre-War policy, however, will (like the British Council) point to the 'Black Years' from 1919 to 1939. Mr Beilby's index totally rebuts their argument. For the period of 1915-1919, agricultural production was 9 per cent lower than it was in 1927-1929, yet the former were the war years when farmers were goaded and coerced to grow the maximum their land would yield. As by 1934-1936 the index reached 110, it follows it gained 19 points in the inter-war period. This represents a 20 per cent increase in production! No other industry of any significant size found it possible to increase output by 20 per cent.

Another notable fact emerges from this index. The war years of 1915-1919 showed an increase in output of only 4 points, from 87 to 91. Yet hundreds of thousands of acres of grassland were ploughed up and returned to wheat, barley and oats. The 'Grow More Food' campaign that the wartime Government enjoined did not, in fact, have the effect of increasing the amount of food grown by more than a modest percentage. We grew more arable crops, but it was at the expense of livestock. The British people ate a higher proportion of home-produced food, but their consumption was reduced and it consisted of less meat, eggs, milk and butter. Mr Beilby's index has been confirmed by all subsequent research. Viscount Astor and Mr B. Seebohm Rowntree in a book entitled *British Agriculture* produced an alternative index, taking gross output instead of Mr Beilby's net output, and using the figures published by the Ministry of Agriculture. Taking 1923 as their base year, they found that by 1936-37 gross agricultural production had increased by 22 per cent. Again, this compares favourably with any other trade or industry.

The Ministry's statistics show that a remarkable expansion took place in all forms of livestock rearing between the wars. Between 1923 and 1939, the population of our herds increased as follows:

Cattle	up by	1,108,000	or	14 per cent
Sheep	up by	5,802,000	or	27 per cent
Pigs	up by	1,401,000	or	45 per cent
Poultry	up by	21,982,000	or	63 per cent

The increase in the number of pigs and poultry is particularly remarkable. Both have been called 'walking cereals', for both consume considerable quantities of corn in one form or another. Low cereal prices were undoubtedly the reason why their numbers rose so dramatically. If the price of cereals had been kept artificially high after the 1914-18 War, at the same level as they had reached during the War as a consequence of enemy action, there would never have been the expansion of the pig herds and poultry flocks. Nor could the cattle and the sheep have been able to return to the fields that had been ploughed up.

Both the consumer and the farmer gained in the process. The consumer in Britain was able to eat meat more cheaply than the consumer in any other industrialised country. Moreover, he was given a variety of choice that was not available anywhere else in the world at comparable prices. As to the farmer, he became the most successful and prosperous in Europe. Sir John Russell, author of *British Farming*, gave the following table to prove the point.

	Output per worker per year		Wages in shillings per week	Livestock units per worker
	Gross £	Net £		
Great Britain	240	200	30.36	10.3
Denmark	180	135	23.26	8.4
Netherlands	150	120	23.30	4.9
Belgium	110	100	18.22	3.4
Switzerland	110	100	27.29	4.3

| France | 90 | 90 | 20.28 | 2.8 |
| Germany | 70 | 70 | 18.23 | 2.8 |

Two facts stand out in that table. The first is that farm wages were immeasurably higher in Great Britain than in Germany – how the tables have turned today! The second is that there is a correlation between the value of output and the quantity of livestock. France and Germany, then as now, believed in growing their own arable crops regardless of the supply in the world market. Quite deliberately, they shut out of their own market wheat and other cereals that could have been exported to them at lower prices. The result was that, unlike us, they were unable to produce meat at a low cost. It was livestock before the War that produced the best returns for farmers, provided only that they were at liberty to buy cereals without paying a tax upon them.

Arable farming is for the larger farmer, livestock for the small farmer. The proposition is almost self-evident. In South Lincolnshire and the Isle of Ely there are some owners of arable small-holdings, but mainly they produce specialist non-cereal crops and, when they do grow corn, they find it necessary to bring in a contractor for harvesting, and even for drilling. Modern machinery for arable farming, not least the combine harvester, now costs so much that a man of few acres cannot make a profitable use of it. On the other hand, livestock benefits from the intensive management and individual care that the small-holder can provide.

The present-day structure of farming militates against livestock and favours the arable sector. Throughout most of the country a general picture can be seen. It is that the average farm is the result of two, three or four pre-war farms having been amalgamated in the last thirty years, probably with the aid of a government subsidy to facilitate the amalgamation. This larger unit is economic for the growing of cereals; and most, perhaps nearly all, its acres will be under plough. It will employ one or two men in the place of five times that number that worked there before the amalgamations took place. There is, of course, one farmer in the place of the several that presided over the separate farms.

108

What were the pressures that caused those others to leave agriculture? Some retired, perhaps content with the price their farm fetched. I suspect they were in the minority. The others were likely to be men skilled with livestock: perhaps in dairying or with pigs or poultry, some were in beef, but a high proportion had several kinds of stock on their farm. They were not specialists, but they were good with animals generally. How many of them still survive? Very few. And how many of them would have survived if we had pursued a policy that had enabled them to buy cereals for their feeding-stuffs in the world market without an import duty or levy placed upon it? The answer must be, very many of them.

In that area of central and southern England that has gone over to the different kinds of livestock farming in the last hundred years, this new structure is everywhere apparent. By previous standards, the farms tend to be large, some 500 acres upwards, and usually the outcome of two or three amalgamations. Each is predominantly arable, heavily mechanised and capital-intensive, having received numerous grants and tax allowances; and in consequence each employs the minimum labour force. Wheat is the favourite crop. It is wheat that is sold by the farmer at 50, 75 or 100 per cent above the price in the market outside the European Community.

The Corn Laws were oppressive, we are told in the history books. Yet today we submit to a tax on corn that is twice as high than it ever was under the Corn Laws! The housewife, in paying more for her bread than she should, does not suffer the price of the livestock farmer. Ever since the Wheat Act and the Import Duties Act of 1934, he has been squeezed. The outcome has been that hundreds of thousands have ceased to be either farmers or farm workers. That there has been such an exodus is no index of the prosperity of an industry.

The evidence points to one conclusion. If the state had not interfered by restricting and taxing cereals from abroad, and if it had not further spent taxpayers' money on a policy that has had the effect of inducing farmers to grow arable crops rather than produce livestock, there would today be more and smaller farms, and more farmers and farm workers.

12/The CAP: Why It Cannot Fit British Farmers

It need hardly be said that there is an obvious reason why a unilateral free trade policy is not practicable for Britain in the immediate future. As members of the EEC we are bound by the terms of the Common Agricultural Policy. Yet how much longer will it survive? It is almost the only common policy that the Community has – and what a basis for a United Europe! It would be difficult to devise a policy more calculated to cause conflict among ten member states. Among those who most ardently desire progress towards the unity of Europe, there is a feeling that it would be sensible to abandon the attempt to merge the conflicting interests of Europe's farmers – which themselves conflict with those of the consumers and further conflict with the interests of our allies in the United States and the Commonwealth – and instead seek to make progress on other policies more conducive to harmony.

It must be completely beyond argument that the CAP puts up the price of food; otherwise there would simply be no need for it to exist. A levy or duty on food imported from abroad is totally unnecessary when its price is higher than the home-grown variety, yet every kind of food grown in the European Community bears some levy or duty when it is imported. This is because food grown in the rest of the EEC is naturally more expensive than it is on the world market.

I say 'the rest of the EEC' with care, for certain commodities we produce can compete against imports, such as potatoes, milk, feed barley, nearly all field vegetables, wheat grown on our better land, eggs, poultry meat and our top quality beef and pork. It is obvious that not all our farmers can compete – they never have and never will – because standards of efficiency vary. Equally there are many farmers on the Continent who could survive happily at world market prices, and none more so than the large producers in the Paris basin. The point is that proportionately very many more of our farmers could prosper with world prices than farmers on the Continent.

Before enlarging on the reasons why our own farmers should be opposed to the CAP, it should be recorded that there is some evidence that the policy may not survive. So long as it takes up from 65 per cent to 75 per cent of the total Community budget, with every possibility that the proportion will rise as the level of food production in the Ten goes up, there is little scope for developing a Community policy in other fields. It could be done by increasing the Community's revenue, but this must be at the expense of the national governments when all of them are under pressure to reduce taxation. The failure to embark upon other policies will not only be demoralising to the officials of the EEC and the protagonists of a United Europe; it could undermine everything that has so far been achieved.

A recession that has clouded over the economy of the whole Common Market, bringing with it a high level of unemployment that promises to go higher still, a standard of living that does not improve and a growth rate that falls below zero, makes a complete nonsense of the Community unless it can be shown that its existence will enable the Ten to overcome the recession more easily as one Community than as separate and independent nation states. The argument is underlined when critics point to other European countries getting out of the recession more swiftly than the Ten.

Which, then, will advance the cause of the EEC further: the CAP being allowed to continue to eat up most of the Community's revenue or the CAP being replaced by national policies for agriculture and the Community's resources being diverted to other policies leading to a speedier exit from the recession? The EEC Commission would like to support the ailing industries of steel, ship building and numerous others that have already made many thousands of their employees redundant and are likely to add, in the next year or two, still more thousands to the ranks of the unemployed. It could also adopt a hundred different ways of stimulating new employment with the funds it would have available. The consequence could be that the Common Market might gain rather more popularity with the electorate than is now the case. As such popularity could persuade public opinion to accept a closer politicial union, this argument is not lost on those who want to see a United States of Europe.

The other threat to the CAP is created by the new members, if Portugal and Spain also join. In both of them, agriculture plays the dominant role in the economy, as it does in Greece; and each of them will need a great deal of financial support. This further strain upon the CAP will take it to breaking point – or beyond. There are people in high places in Brussels who have already concluded that their entry into the EEC will be a convenient time to dissolve the CAP.

The CAP has no friends left in Britain – except among the policy makers of the NFU and, in muted accents, the Country Landowners' Association. Even our own efficient farmers are beginning to see some compelling reasons why they should oppose the policy as forthrightly as any housewife now harrassed by rising prices. Let us now look at them.

The efficient farmer should be permitted to expand. Expansion has been and still is a key word for our farmers. The record since the war shows that only by expanding production, year after year, have they been able to make a reasonable livelihood. It is now becoming apparent that this expansion cannot continue in a Community swamped by surpluses, unless the excess supplies are exported abroad. However, the world market prices for every commodity we grow best are lower than the prices in the Common Market. This means that they can only be sold outside on the world market if they are given an export subsidy. In other words, the taxpayer in the Common Market must pay the difference between the world market price and the Common Market price. Already the taxpayer is burdened by these export subsidies to the tune of more than £3,000,000,000 a year, i.e. about £15 per head of the population. Anyone who expects him to go on paying an ever-increasing amount to subsidise butter, wheat, beef and other foodstuffs for other nations like the Russians and Eastern Europeans to eat must not be surprised if the taxpaying worm eventually turns, denounces the whole system of subsidising foreigners' food as Alice in Wonderland nonsense, and in his wrath demands that it should cease forthwith. If that were to happen, farmers in the Common Market would face a major crisis.

But there is another reason why we cannot export an increasing amount of food at subsidised prices. It is dumping. Of all the countries or blocs in the world, none has been more guilty of dumping in recent years than the EEC. One of the reasons why the United States – the country than can produce wheat in large quantities more cheaply and efficiently than any other – has cut back production by about 20 per cent is because the Common Market is unloading some 3,000,000 tons of wheat onto the world market at a price far below the cost of production. The Americans realise that the production of wheat is increasing in the Common Market and that this unfair competition is likely to intensify. Will the United States continue to remain patiently silent if her farmers are driven out of business? Or may they in self-defence put up barriers against our exports to her? Indeed the answer is that the United States has already resorted to such barriers against our exports.

Numerous other countries are equally concerned at this dumping. The Prime Minister of Australia, in a speech in the City of London, has declared it a certain fact that the policy of the Common Market has directly caused a third of the Australian dairy farmers to be deprived of their livelihood and forced to give up dairy farming because they are no longer allowed to export their butter and cheese to the United Kingdom. As they were able to produce both items more cheaply than producers in the Common Market, their feelings of bitterness are understandable.

Also in Australia, no less than 80,000 beef cattle have been shot and their carcasses burnt because the world market for beef has been undermined by the Common Market policy of subsidising its exports. In Argentina a worse story can be told. Their beef has been available at the lowest economic price but no sale abroad can be assured while this dumping continues, so production has plummeted down to a fraction of what it was and could be still. While the Argentinian can have a steak on his

113

table for ten pence, the housewife in Britain pays twice as much as the world price.

Brazil, Uruguay, Canada, South Africa, Kenya, New Zealand are also on the list of major food producers who have the soil and the climate that enable them to supply the world market at the lowest prices. But they are being forced to reduce production. Their farmers are growing less, and many are giving up altogether. Tens of thousands of their employees have lost their jobs. For most of them, there is no other work available and they have suffered real hardship, particularly in the South American countries, but also in Canada and New Zealand where the recession is beginning to bite deeply. In these countries many, many thousands of acres are producing less than they could or are not being farmed at all.

Murmurings of protest are just being heard. Perhaps some of these countries will not be able to retaliate in self-defence as the United States is doing, but it is unrealistic to expect them to suffer the continued and increasing amount of dumping with complacency. It is not impossible that they will gang up together – maybe not all of them, but a decisive number of them – and when they do, enough pressure, moral as well as economic, will be applied to force the Common Market to bring to an end its policy of dumping surplus foodstuffs onto the world market at prices far below the cost of production.

Yet the EEC is driven to dumping so long as its target of self-sufficiency is exceeded. Every kind of food that British farmers produce to any significant extent is now in surplus in the Common Market. Wheat, barley, sugar, poultry meat, milk, cheese and butter are all now produced in quantities far in excess of internal demand. Beef, eggs and pigmeat may, in a few years, get into a similar state of surplus.

The production of these foods is increasing rather than diminishing, and it is really out of the question to add still more to the vast quantities that are already being stored in intervention. Besides, the existing storage places are nearly all filled to capacity. Hence the need to export, but as the world price of all those foodstuffs is lower than the price they are sold for economically in the Common Market, it follows that the export of every important kind of food that we produce in

Britain is a case of dumping.

What then is the future of the British farmer when governed by the Common Agricultural Policy? Spokesmen for the NFU assert that British farmers are entitled to expand because they are more efficient and that their counterparts on the Continent should be required to stand aside if their standards of efficiency are lower. In a Common Market, first prize should go to the man who deserves it most.

To us that may seem common sense. The only flaw in the argument is that CAP is founded upon 'the principle of Community preference'. The essence of this is that we are bound to adjust our fiscal and other policies so that consumers exercise a preference for Community-produced food rather than what is available from other countries. Of course, the Common Market can change the mechanisms of the Common Agricultural Policy in order to encourage the efficient and discourage the inefficient, but any change of consequence is made by the Council of Ministers. This means that Ministers of Agriculture of each of the ten member states would have to agree to alter the system in favour of the efficient. Unfortunately, a majority of the ten ministers represent countries where inefficient farming is profitable, and must remain so for electoral reasons. There is an obvious correlation between the number of small, inefficient farmers and smallholders and the voting power of the agricultural community. Less than 3 per cent of the British electorate are engaged in agriculture: their votes do not matter very much. In France, Germany and Italy the Ministers of Agriculture know that whenever they attend the Council of Ministers they must later be answerable to millions of voters whose continued existence and prosperity depend upon what is settled in Brussels.

There is no evidence that the Danish or the Dutch Minister of Agriculture will be encouraged to support any British proposals to change the system. While it is true that agriculture in Denmark and the Netherlands is of a high standard of efficiency, both the Danes and the Dutch are beneficiaries of the CAP as it is now functioning. In neither of those countries is there any pressure on the Minister of Agriculture to act in a way that would be favourable to us. Experience in recent years shows that much the same can be said of Belgium, Luxemburg and Ireland. As for Greece, a major argument for her joining the Common Market was that Greek agriculture, the dominant industry, would flourish with the extra support of the CAP.

The conclusion must be drawn that any British Minister will be in a minority of one in calling for the kind of changes that are necessary in the CAP if British agriculture is to expand so as to displace imports of food from the rest of the Common Market. Let us never forget that when Mr Heath went over to Paris to meet M. Pompidou at the time when France was still putting obstacles in the way of our entry, he was told by the French President that France would support our application to join on certain conditions, and one of them was that Britain would sever her links with her traditional trading partners in the Commonwealth and instead buy her food from within the Common Market. M. Pompidou subsequently broadcast to the French people an account of their interview, making it plain that he had insisted upon that promise before he lifted the French veto upon our membership. Mr Heath has since refused to comment upon whether it was true or not.

Even if the inefficient farmers on the Continent were driven off their farms, what would it avail our own farmers? It is arguable that they would be very much worse off. There are several parts of the Common Market which are farmed as intensively and as skilfully as anywhere in the British Isles. The Paris basin is one such area. Yields of wheat, sugar beet and other crops are fully comparable with our best. Twenty years ago, perhaps even ten years ago, the story was different; then they were behind us structurally and technically. What has happened in the Paris basin, in the Po Valley and elsewhere is beginning to be repeated over a wide area of Western Europe.

It will be a long time before they all catch up with us, but there is no doubt that as their farms amalgamate and modern machinery is used and intensive fertilisers applied, as well as all the other aids with which we are familiar, their productivity must increase. Roy Jenkins, when President of the EEC Commission, has spoken of this great scope for expansion in Continental Europe. Addressing the Food Manufacturers

Association in London on 27 September 1977, he said:

> European agriculture has tremendous productive potential: if average yields of crops and livestock were brought up to the levels of the most efficient the increases in output would be enormous. But if nobody wants to consume the additional output, if there is no market for it, we shall have wasted our resources. That is why I am convinced that we must take more and more account of future demand for food, and for different types of food, in Europe.

If it is a fair generalisation that most agriculture in Western Europe is in the state ours was in, say, thirty years ago, then it is likely that given another ten years they could be, acre for acre, producing as much as we are now.

This could have a devastating effect upon our farmers. Let two examples explain. A herd of twenty milking cows is still profitable on the Continent, as it was thirty year ago in Britain but no longer is – in fact many profitable herds are even smaller. As events are now moving, herds on the other side of the Channel will, ten years hence, be getting as large as ours are now. Milk production will be reaching fantastic levels. Who will drink it all?

As it is, there is a chronic glut of milk and dairy products in the Common Market, and the total cost of subsidising the dairy farmers is approaching £2,700,000,000. More than 40 per cent of this vast handout is likely to be spent on what they euphemistically describe as export restitutions, but the rest of the world calls dumping. The journal *Agra Europe* has estimated, in a detailed survey published in June 1981, that the present cost of supporting the EEC dairy farmers will rise to £5,400 millions in four years unless the system is reformed. The present surplus of 10 per cent, they say, will rise to 17 per cent as a result of improved productivity. As *Agra Europe* has a reputation for competent research and accurate forecasting, this increase in the cost of support, which is just 100 per cent, deserves careful attention.

The potential for wheat growing in the rest of the Common Market is also immense. British farmers overlook at their peril the vast acres of top quality land that abound in Western Europe. In Germany alone there are hundreds of thousands of

117

acres capable of high yields of cereals which are so far nowhere near their real potential. Much of this land is under grass, as it has been for generations, in small-holdings where combine harvesters are unknown and even tractors have yet to be used, but every ounce of the soil is waiting to respond to modern methods of cereal production.

It seems obvious that no British Minister of Agriculture attending the Council of Ministers, where the CAP is formulated, can, like some latter-day Luddite, insist that life should stand still over this vast area of Western Europe. Many millions of pounds worth of aid, from both national and Common Market funds, is being poured into these areas to enable them to catch up with us. We in Britain, who have had our own period of expansion ever since 1939, which has brought a transformation in all our farming practices – the triumph of the second Agricultural Revolution – are in no position to say to our partners in Europe, 'Thou shalt not do as we have done.'

As the Common Market is already more than self-sufficient in temperate foods, and as the consumption of these foods is static, its supply must find its outlet in the world market. But this is just not possible unless we resort to dumping. Are we to pour onto the world market an ever-increasing quantity of butter, wheat, sugar and other foods to be bought at below the cost of production, subsidised at the expense of our taxpayers, while the low-cost producers of the world are driven off their farms?

In the face of these facts it is difficult to see how the technically efficient British farmer is going to be encouraged to expand. A British Government might wish to support an expansionist policy and be willing to offer a range of grants, subsidies and other aids to underwrite such a policy. Yet the whole purpose of the Common Agricultural Policy – which means what it says, a policy common to and binding upon each of the member states – is that all national aids to agriculture should go out of the window and be replaced by a common system applicable to all. It is inconceivable that the Council of Ministers will ever lift their collective finger to encourage British farmers to expand any further so long as the others lag behind in productivity.

The tragedy is that the efficient British farmer could get into a desperate position if he does not expand. The rate of inflation may or may not fall, but some inflation will certainly continue. The cost of every single item purchased for the farm goes up year after year. The trend must continue for some years yet. Tractors, combines, ploughs and all other machinery steadily go up in price, as also does the cost of keeping them in repair. Wages cannot stand still; all forms of transport become remorselessly more expensive. In perhaps three years from now, these various costs could be 20 per cent, 30 per cent or more higher than they are now. Higher costs can be met either by higher farmgate prices or by increased production. There is no third way. Now if farmers are to be deprived of the chance to increase production, it is far from certain whether they will be fully compensated by higher prices. Consumers are resisting by changing their eating habits.

The National Food Survey, based on how 7,000 families eat, and published by the Ministry of Agriculture, shows how we are becoming very sensitive to price changes. It shows trends that are especially serious for all our arable farmers. Our consumption of bread has fallen to 31.25 ounces per person per week on average in 1981, from 35.76 ounces ten years previously (a fall of 12.61 per cent); and sugar, 11.08 ounces instead of 15.80 ounces (a fall of 29.87 per cent); and potatoes 41.87 ounces instead of 51.84, a fall of 19.23 per cent.

This decline in consumption is remarkably steep over a comparatively short period of time. It should be enough to shatter any complacency in Agriculture House. But it is not the most serious aspect of the change in our food consumption so far as the arable farmer is concerned. Since about 90 per cent of our grain crop goes to feeding not humans but livestock, he has a considerable interest in the sales of milk, butter and eggs. These have gone down quite rapidly; and in the case of milk, it seems that every increase in the price on the doorstep is marked by a decided drop in the number of bottles bought. The National Food Survey shows that the total amount of milk consumed in 1971 was 4.46 pints on average for each person every week, but in 1981 the comparable figure was 4.01. That is a fall of 10.08 per cent. In the case of butter, it went down from

5.53 ounces to 3.69 ounces – no less than 33.27 per cent. 4.55 eggs were eaten on average each week per person in 1971; in 1981 it was 3.68, a decline of 19.12 per cent. Consumption of cheese went up, from 3.63 to 3.89 ounces, but the increase of 6.68 per cent is small consolation when so much of it is imported from other parts of the EEC.

The demand for our home-produced milk is likely to decline still more once the French are allowed to supply our market with their UHT milk. The House of Commons Select Committee on Agriculture carried out an inquiry over several months into this risk; and the evidence it heard showed that this milk would probably retail at two pence a pint less than our own. Such strong competition could have a devastating effect upon both our own dairy farmers and the cereal producers. The Minister of Agriculture has succeeded in keeping out this milk on grounds of hygiene, but the Select Committee found that argument difficult to sustain. The European Court of Justice is to decide whether we may continue the ban.

The fall in consumption highlights one particular fallacy above all. Before we entered the EEC our farmers were told again and again that the levies and duties under the CAP would close the door on cheap food from the Commonwealth and our other traditional suppliers and home-produced food would fill the gap. The British housewife, it was assumed, would go on buying the same kinds of food, but at a higher price. The assumption has been proved wrong and the British farmer has not gained the outlet in our market that he was promised.

That habits of a life-time are changing is the unanimous view of the retail food trade. Bacon, for example, is no longer placed on the breakfast table as a matter of course; the Sunday joint is a ritual no longer; and pastas have ousted some of our traditional foodstuffs. For a generation we have lived with steadily higher food prices without changing the pattern of our consumption, but it now looks as if housewives, and even industrial caterers, will react to any substantial increases in prices with either a reduction in their purchases or a switch to cheaper kinds of food.

Waiting in the wings are the manufacturers of synthetic meat. Schools, factories and hospitals have already become large buyers. Given another five years' research in the laboratories, it is likely that the manufacturers will be able to offer the public kinds of meat which will so resemble the real thing that many families will opt for them, although they would spurn such dishes today. We may assume that these synthetic alternatives will never displace the good quality natural meats, but most of the meat we eat today is not in that category. It is, therefore, of fundamental importance to all livestock farmers that they should not have their produce made artificially more expensive than it need be. The Common Agricultural Policy does just that.

Only one conclusion can be drawn. The British farmer is sliding along a series of ratchets. While we continue to submit to an agricultural policy common to ten countries, all of which have interests in conflict with ours, our farmers will be taken along a route that will inexorably make it more difficult for them to maintain their present livelihoods. Some will be complacent about it: they will turn over and go to sleep. Those British farmers who look further ahead, who can envisage what the CAP will bring by the end of the 1980s, will stir themselves now.

13/The Truth about Protection

The French economist, Frederic Bastiat, in his *Essays on Political Economy*, listed twelve forms of Government interference under the heading 'What is Seen and What is Not Seen'. One was protectionism. What is seen about protection – what is clearly visible and calculable to us all – is the way it supports a particular branch of our economy. What is not seen, being invisible and incalculable, is the effect it has on all the other branches of the economy. The effect must be to weaken and impoverish, at least to some extent, those parts of the economy that do not share in the protection.

From them capital, land, labour and natural resources must tend to be diverted. This diversion is always away from what the consumer would prefer and in the direction of what he does not prefer. Unless it has those effects, there is no purpose in giving protection to any industry. So it follows that protection must always work against the wishes and interests of the consumer. the hope that they will make us believe otherwise, at least so far as food is concerned.

A large part of this book has been devoted to rebutting those arguments. Protectionism is, and can only be, an onslaught upon the consumer's freedom of choice. But free trade provides and guarantees that freedom. If the consumer's preference is diverted, so that he is induced to spend his money in a way that does not follow his natural inclination, those industries and other branches of the economy which are able and willing to supply his real wants will receive less of his money and will thus be less able to succeed. The longer a policy of protection is continued, the more such industries are adversely affected, the adverse effects being cumulative. It is a process of impoverishment; and sooner or later everyone is the poorer.

The process is part of what Monsieur Bastiat described as what is not seen. We cannot quantify the number of businesses that have been made bankrupt as a result of a policy that has made food artificially more expensive than it need be, forcing the British people to spend more money on food, and therefore less on other items. Nor can we specify how many of the present number of unemployed are out of a job because of this policy. The only bedrock of certainty is that the longer this process of impoverishment goes on, the more people are likely to be made bankrupt or unemployed.

If the evidence in this book is correct, there are just two kinds of beneficiaries of the present policy. The first are the arable farmers, principally in central and southern England, who have land that is not fitted for cereal crops and who can only derive a livelihood from them when a high tariff is erected against corn imported from more favourable soils and climates. Farmers in the traditional arable areas of East Anglia are not, of course, in this category. The other beneficiaries are those large companies who supply machinery and fertilisers to the arable sector.

But even these beneficiaries are not exempt from an economic law that permits no exception. It is immutable and it works inexorably. It is this: divert capital, labour and enterprise from where the consumers would wish them to be, and all consumers are afforded steadily less and less satisfaction. The longer the process goes on, the more impoverished the whole community becomes. Eventually, the beneficiaries of protection themselves are pulled down into the deepening abyss of poverty.

One question remains. How much longer will the British people allow this policy to drag them down?

14/Summary

THE TRIUMPH

Agriculture's triumph has been threefold. An area the size of Yorkshire, Lancashire, Durham and Northumberland combined, previously uneconomic for the growing of cereals, has been brought into arable cultivation. Productivity on the land has increased more than in any other substantial industry, so that one man produces food enough for forty-two people. Between 1954 and 1981 the yield of wheat to the acre has increased by 98 per cent, barley by 62 per cent, and sugar by 23 per cent. The average dairy cow produces 48 per cent more milk and the hen 52 per cent more eggs.

Technically, it is an achievement that verges upon the miraculous. A triumph, indeed.

AND THE SHAME

On the date this is written (30 July 1982), the levy on wheat imported from abroad is £73.50 a tonne, which is a tax of nearly 100 per cent. On maize, it is £66.17 a tonne, which is a tax of over 100 per cent. These high taxes on the consumer make it profitable for farmers to grow wheat and other cereals on land unsuitable for such cultivation – Grade III land or worse – as Appendix 1 indicates.

The consumer is worse off by £3,000 millions a year; this is the difference between the price of food in the world market and the Common Market (about £5 a week per family). On top of that, the taxpayer has paid out, since 1946, a total of some £40,000 millions, in 1982 terms, for expenditure by the Ministry of Agriculture for the benefit of farmers.

The value of agricultural land has been forced up artificially by the same amount, £40,000 millions (which may not be a coincidence), after making full allowance for the effect of

124

inflation, so that landowners have become that much richer. If there are as many as a hundred thousand landowners, it is £400,000 each. The value of the very best land does not seem to have risen in real terms: the worse the land, the more its value has been inflated.

The diversion of capital to agriculture from businesses and industries that are efficient, in the sense that they do not need subsidies and can pay their share of taxation, runs into yet more thousands of millions of pounds. The diversion of capital this year alone equals the capital of thirteen companies the size of Courtaulds. Whether it has the effect of closing down thirteen companies the size of Courtaulds is arguable; certainly it has deprived some efficient industries of the capital they need for their growth and development and so made them less efficient. The consequent loss of jobs caused by this diversion of over £3,000 millions each year is incalculable: one million, two million, or is it more? The TUC has claimed that a reflation of £5,000 millions would end the problem of unemployment, and the CBI seems not to have dissented from that view.

Banks have lent a further £4,000 millions to farmers, principally to large-scale owner-occupiers rather than to tenants or small farmers – in preference to other businesses in need of fresh capital.

Pension funds and insurance companies have also diverted their investments into agriculture and away from other industries in recent years to the extent of hundreds of millions of pounds.

Taxpayers' support for agriculture has steadily increased as a percentage of farmers' incomes; and it is likely to continue to rise. It is now 166 per cent. Yet 60,000 farmers have gone out of business in about ten years. This is because the system tends to encourage large-scale cereal growing and it penalises (literally so, for his feedingstuffs are taxed) the livestock farmer.

The millionaire can avoid capital transfer tax altogether, provided he buys a farm. The tax allowances are so favourable that the average farmer pays only 15 per cent of his income in tax. That is the same as the average farm-worker, although more than one-third of the farm-workers are poor enough to receive the family income supplement. Before the war, British agriculture was prosperous enough to make our farm-workers the highest paid in Europe. Then they were paid 50 per cent more than those in France or Germany. Now they are paid less than their counterparts in either of those countries.

Increasing productivity has transferred jobs from the countryside to the cities. 90,000 farm-workers have lost their direct employment on the land in about ten years and been displaced by equipment and machinery made in cities, most of it imported from abroad.

This process of rural depopulation has changed much of the face of the countryside. So has the uprooting of countless woodlands and hedgerows and the demolition of many farmhouses and farm buildings to make way for new concrete, factory-type constructions, necessary for large-scale arable farming. Many tens of thousands of acres of downland and moorland have been lost to the public for their recreation; and the public has had to pay for their loss.

Much of the increased productivity is due to the massive increase in the use of fertilisers. A high proportion has to be imported. This has two serious consequences for the Third World. The increased demand has forced up the price, making it more difficult for poorer countries to afford the fertilisers they need. Worse than that, the supply of some of these artificial fertilisers is not infinite, and in years to come they will prove scarce and difficult to extract. Rather than apply such vast quantities on to the poorer quality land here, it would be more sensible to safeguard these resources by keeping them available for more suitable land in the Third World.

By a policy that strives for self-sufficiency, we have cut off trading links with numerous countries; thus many of our export markets have been lost, and our other industries have suffered. While it is true that among non-Communist countries trade is not conducted on bilateral terms, it remains broadly the case that the more one country imports from another, the more it will export to it. By putting up trade barriers against the United States, Canada, Latin America, Australia and New Zealand, we suffer grievous self-inflicted wounds, for those are the countries with the greatest potential for the expansion of trade. Not so many years ago, we were Argentina's best customer; had we continued to buy her beef and wheat on the scale we used to do before we entered the Common Market, it is unthinkable that her junta would have risked her most important market by invading the Falklands.

The poorer developing countries have suffered grievously by our protectionist policy, and none more than those dependent upon sugar for their foreign exchange. The irony is they can produce it cheaper than the Common Market, yet the latter dumps such a large proportion of the world's supply at prices so far below its own or anyone else's cost of production that these poorer countries are compelled to sell their own sugar at a huge loss. So the debts of the developing countries pile up, and the world banking system (which is our banking system) is placed under such severe strain that it is seriously said that it may not survive.

The more we impoverish the world's poor by our selfish policies (and self-sufficiency is selfish by definition), the more they are likely to listen to the overtures of Communism. Any regular visitor to Third World countries can corroborate how this is happening with incontestible evidence. Politically and strategically, it is important that this alienation of the Third World should not continue. It is absurd to say we should support agriculture to the extent that we do because, as is claimed so often, 'all countries support their agriculture'. The developed countries generally give support to their farmers, although it is doubtful whether any are as protected as those in the Common Market, but developing countries cannot do so. Developing countries are so-called because their other industries are not developed: generally speaking, agriculture is their one main industry. Agriculture has, in their case, to support the government. Only in developed countries with prosperous industries able to give revenue to the government can the government, in its turn, support agriculture.

Nearly half of the world's arable land is uncultivated. This includes many millions of acres of land that we would classify as Grade I or II. Amid this rich land that lies idle are countless thousands of people too poor to buy the food that it is capable of growing. They have no income because they have no work. Living in developing countries, agriculture is their primary industry. But food will not be grown unless there is someone able to buy it. The old imperial masters (the French, the Germans, the Dutch, the Italians and the British) refashioned the agricultural economies of most of those countries, so that they might receive their supplies of food; now they have banded together to enforce a policy that permits only a little of it to feed the people in Western Europe. Most of that little is tropical foodstuffs that do not compete with their own farmers' produce.

By re-opening our doors to the food which they and the rest of the world are capable of producing more cheaply than we can, British agriculture would gain in the long term. In the short term there would indeed be losers, who fall into three categories. First, the landowners and farmers whose assets have been so grossly inflated. Then the banks and pension funds that have chosen to lend their money or have it invested in large-scale arable farming rather than other industries. The other losers are those capital-intensive, rather than labour-intensive, companies that service and supply arable farmers, like Shell and ICI.

Arable farming would continue in a prosperous state on land suitable for it (generally Grades I and II), providing our needs in the way of field vegetables and some cereals. Other cereals, particularly those required for livestock feeding, would be imported at about half their present cost.

Livestock farming would gain immeasurably. More farms, smaller farms and part-time farms would follow; opportunities for the young farmer (now dismal) would be considerable, especially if he could only afford to begin on his own in a small way.

This transformation of the farming pattern would make the countryside look different – more as we used to know it. Life in the country would be reinvigorated by the infusion of more farmers.

Agriculture would cease to be a lame and diseased duck requiring ever larger injections of public money to sustain it in a state of euphoria. Farmers would be efficient, by any yardstick that could be found.

No longer beholden to politicians, they would gain the dignity of independence.

Appendices

Appendix 1/The Classification of Land

The Minister of Agriculture is actively looking at ways in which he can reclassify the grades of agricultural land. His prime object is to remove from Grade III land the stigma of being 'third class'. As 48.9 per cent of all agricultural land is in this category, the change would be of some importance to agriculture. Undoubtedly, it has some relevance in the discussion about whether this type of land should be used for arable crops on the scale that it is at present.

The Minister has proposed that the existing five grades should become three. Grades I, II and III he wishes to renumber IA, IB and IC respectively, while Grade IV becomes Grade II and Grade V, Grade III. The boundaries of the grades are to remain precisely the same. Far from weakening the argument in this book, this change underlines what has taken place – the transformation of inferior land into land of great value at a severe cost to the British people.

In a Written Answer in the House of Commons on 5 May 1981, about these changes, the Parliamentary Secretary to the Ministry insisted that the first three grades are 'prime agricultural land'. The Ministry in a letter that went out in April 1981 spoke of Grade III land as being 'highly productive agricultural land'. This description conflicts with the First Progress Report of the Ministry's Study Group on Agricultural Land Classification. The Study Group consisted of twelve experts drawn from the Ministry and its views, published in 1966, were accepted by the Minister and were not, so far as I can find out, challenged by anyone. Indeed, their classification of land has continued until today.

This is their definition of Grade III land: 'Land of average quality with limitations due to the soil, relief or climate'. After describing its defects, they conclude: 'In fact, some of the best quality permanent grassland may be placed in this Grade, where the physical characteristics of the land make arable cropping inadvisable.' A sensible agricultural policy would ensure that such good quality grassland would remain pasture, but it is the very opposite that has happened.

The Study Group defined Grade IV land as 'Land with severe limitations due to adverse soil, relief or climate. . . . Generally only suitable for low output enterprises.' Land even in this category has been used for growing high-cost wheat.

Appendix 2/Calculating the Cost of the CAP to the British People

The prolonged dispute about how much Britain should contribute to the revenue of the EEC has focussed some attention upon the cost of the CAP, but it has failed to give the British people a clear view of the true burden it places upon them. Being the only policy of the Community fully in effect, the CAP naturally claims the greatest proportion of the expenditure. But supposing that proportion to be 70 per cent in any one year and Britain's net contribution to the EEC budget to be £1 billion, it would be a mistake to assume (as many do assume) that the true and total cost of the CAP to the British people was only £700 millions.

The assumption is mistaken for two reasons. First, people in Britain make contributions to and receive payments from the EEC not only in their role as taxpayers but also as consumers and producers. If a British consumer bought wheat from France rather than from outside the Community the likely consequence would be a reduction in the amount received in import levies from the UK and in the amount paid out in restitutions to the exporting country. There would be no change in the amount of money transferred from the UK to EEC producers, but because the mechanics differ Britain's apparent budgetary contribution would fall and so would France's budgetary receipts.

Secondly, these budgetary calculations ignore the inter-relationship of trade flows and budgetary mechanisms. For example, Belgium and Holland are contributors to the EEC budget of amounts of import levies and common customs duties quite disproportionate to their VAT contributions or their size. This is simply because a high proportion of EEC imports enter the Community via Antwerp and Rotterdam. There is no possibility that the Belgian and Dutch governments could successfully levy these tariffs on what are predominantly imports into Germany if import duties were retained by member governments rather than remitted centrally. There is, therefore, no sense in which the passing on of these receipts represents a budgetary contribution by Holland or Belgium. They are, in fact, levies on German consumers.

An attempt must therefore be made at a comprehensive assessment of the gains and losses from the CAP to consumers, producers and taxpayers in each member country of the EEC. To do this, it is necessary to define some bench-mark against which these gains and losses are measured. In measuring the gains and losses to individual countries, it is supposed that in the absence of collective arrangements, such as the CAP, trade between countries would take place at world prices. In the absence of altruism, this would immediately follow. Consumer losses and producer gains will also be measured relative to the position that would arise if trade took place at world prices. In the absence of arrangements for agricultural protection these are what consumers could expect to pay and what producers could expect to receive. These arguments beg the question of what such world prices would be; but it is important to establish first that they represent the appropriate standard against which to compare the resource flows of the CAP.

The consequences of a policy such as the CAP are illustrated in Figure 1. The curve DD shows a country's demands for an agricultural commodity at different prices. SS represents domestic supply. As prices rise, more producers are attracted to this particular commodity and so domestic output would be AB. At the world price, domestic demand is AC and the balance, BC, would be imported.

Now suppose an import levy AA' is imposed which raises the domestic price to A'. Since domestic farmers can obtain a higher price for their output, domestic supply expands to A'B'. At the same time, the rise in price reduces domestic demand to A'C'. The contraction in demand and increase in supply reduce imports sharply to B'C'. The additional amount paid· by consumers is AA' on output A'C', so that their loss is

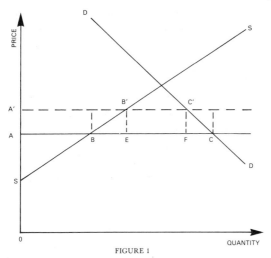

FIGURE 1

measured by the area A'C'F A. This loss is divided between the
extra income accruing to domestic producers A'B'EA and the
government's receipts of import levies B'C'FE.

Thus our basic measures of loss and gain are: producer gain,
A'B'EA; taxpayer gain, B'C'FE; consumer loss, A'C'FA.
However, two additional sources of loss should be noted. Not
all of the increase in producer income from the levy flows into
net farm profits, because the additional output that the levy
induces necessarily has a production cost higher than the world
price A (otherwise it would have been produced anyway). The
triangle BEB' is a measure of the extra cost of this additional
output and should be subtracted from the measure of producer
gain. In addition, consumers lose not simply because of the
additional amounts which they pay for the commodities they
continue to buy, but also because the price rise discourages
their consumption. They eat less beef and butter because there
are occasions on which they are willing to pay OA, but not OA'
for these goods. This loss on goods that are no longer consumed
is, of course, not reflected in any compensating gain to
producers. The loss is measured by the triangle CFC'.

The consequence is that the net gains and losses from the
policy do not sum to zero; the overall losses exceed the gain.
The first of the sources of net loss – which occurs because
domestic output is on average more costly than world

135

output – arises whatever method of protection is adopted. The second – the consumer loss – arises because domestic prices are raised and comes about only under the levy system. It would not occur if the alternative method of farm price support – direct subsidies to producers – were employed. However, as there are net costs, in terms of work disincentives and the like, to raising tax revenue for agricultural subsidies, the choice between these two approaches is not as clear-cut as the argument at first suggests.

In Figure 1 the rise in domestic prices was not large enough to bring about self-sufficiency. But Europe is, in fact, self-sufficient in a majority of agricultural products. The case of self-sufficiency is illustrated in Figure 2. Here domestic output has expanded to A'B' while demand has fallen to A'C'. There is now surplus production of C'B'. In order to maintain a price A', this must be removed from the market, either by exporting it or by purchases into intervention. In order to export it, it is necessary to pay a subsidy of A'A since the surplus will not realise a price higher than A on world markets. In this case, the loss to consumers is A'C'FA. The gain to producers is A'B'EA. The difference between the two is made up of export restitutions of C'B'EF. It should be noticed that the budgetary gains from levies in Figure 1 are turned by self-sufficiency into budgetary costs in Figure 2. Again, there are 'triangle losses' to producers of BB'E and to consumers of CC'F, and a net loss overall.

Where the commodity is purchased into intervention it is necessary to attach some value to intervention stocks. There are two extreme views – one is that these stocks simply represent temporary surpluses which can be disposed of at Community prices in due course; the other is that these stocks have negative value: there is little prospect of ever selling them, they cannot simply be destroyed because of the political outcry that would result, and they involve a continuing and increasing bill for storage. This bill for storage is now substantial. Intervention stocks are valued at world prices, so that a purchase into intervention, like an export, is taken to involve net expenditure by the Community of AA'. This probably underestimates the losses which result.

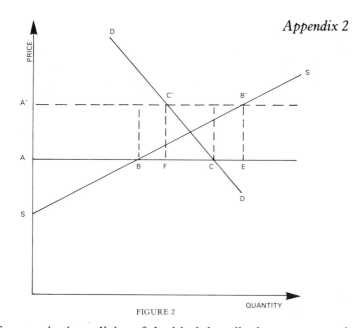

FIGURE 2

If protectionist policies of the kind described were operated nationally, then the losses to consumers would be offset by the gains to producers, except for the triangles that have been identified. Under the financial mechanisms of the CAP, however, levies are a Community receipt and restitutions and interventions are Community expenditures. So any one country will be a net contributor when its domestic consumption exceeds its domestic production and a net beneficiary when it is self-sufficient. Overall gains and losses will be determined by the degree of self-sufficiency and the gap between the domestic and the world prices; a large gap is detrimental to a country which is less than self-sufficient and advantageous to one which is more than self-sufficient. In this respect the UK, Germany and Italy are significant losers and the Netherlands, Denmark and Ireland are beneficiaries.

So far, 'world prices' of agricultural products have been spoken of as though these were readily available pieces of information. However, there are few commodities in which there is now a substantial free trade, and there are major problems in practice and in principle in deciding what is the appropriate measure of world prices to use.

The practical problem is one of determining what current

137

'world prices' are. There are three principal sources. First, a measure of the world price of each commodity is implicit in the CAP itself, since the levy is set so as to bridge the gap between world prices and Community prices. Thus world prices can be estimated by subtracting levies from Community selling prices. Unfortunately, it is notorious that for a number of commodities, particularly beef, the levy is set at a figure much in excess of what is necessary to make imports uncompetitive, and imports of beef are, in fact, negligible. Export restitutions may provide a more reliable guide, but are subject to the opposite bias. Second, the Commission records 'third country offer prices', but it is not always the case that these reflect realistic offers of substantial quantities. Thirdly, we can measure the prices at which other countries, particularly the United States, do in fact import agricultural products.

The problem of principle arises because the existing world prices reflect existing trade flows which are themselves, in part, the result of the CAP. We therefore need to consider how these flows would change, and what the consequential effect on prices would be, in the absence of the CAP. To do this, it is necessary to consider what agricultural policies would exist if the CAP did not. However, one of the essential points made in this book is that farmers throughout the world have the capacity and the willingness to grow a great deal more food than they do now; and this additional supply can match the substantially increased demand at existing prices. Even if the absurd were to happen and Britain were to decide to buy every ounce of her food from the world market, the demand could be met by increasing world production by a fraction of one per cent.

From the preceding analysis the principal resource flows resulting from the operation of the CAP are as follows:

(i)   Losses to consumers from higher prices, which are equal to domestic consumption multiplied by the differences between domestic and world prices;

(ii) Losses to consumers by the reduction in demand for agricultural products relative to such demands at world prices;

(iii) Gains to producers from high prices, which are equal to domestic production multiplied by the difference between domestic and world prices;

(iv) Additional costs incurred by producers of output which would not be economic at world prices;

(v) The net budgetary contribution to agricultural support derived from taxes on non-agricultural products. This is equal to expenditure on export restitutions, net of levies, plus expenditure on intervention, storage and guidance, less the value of additions to intervention stock.